Creative Growth Games

Creative Growth Games

BY
EUGENE RAUDSEPP
WITH
GEORGE P. HOUGH, JR.

A PERIGEE BOOK

Perigee Books
are published by
G.P. Putnam's Sons
200 Madison Avenue
New York, New York, 10016

First Perigee Printing, 1980

ISBN: 0-399-50415-X

Printed in the United States of America

CONTENTS

v

The creative imagination is as potent as the forces of nature.

Every authentic individual is a creative person.

Creative activity ennobles man's joy and blunts the edge of his suffering.

The person who is endowed with the spirit of divine discontent, moves forward; the person who is satisfied with the status quo, moves backward.

The only frontiers that can never be conquered are the creative frontiers of the mind.

Acknowledgments

It would be difficult to individually acknowledge all the people whose stimulating researches and evocative formulations inspired many of the games and exercises in this book. Of particular relevance have been the insights offered in the works of J. P. Guilford, Alex F. Osborn, Sidney J. Parnes, Edward de Bono, John E. Arnold, Alvin L. Simberg, Ross L. Mooney, George M. Prince, and William J. J. Gordon.

Grateful acknowledgment is made to the following for permission to quote selections from their works: to James L. Adams and the San Francisco Book Company, Inc., for items appearing in "Breaking Out," from *Conceptual Blockbusting*, © 1976 by James L. Adams, San Francisco: San Francisco Book Company, 1976; for items in "Fun with Puns" to Dr. Marvin Karlins and the *Journal of Psychology* from "A Note on a New Test of Creativity," *Journal of Psychology*, 1967, Vol. 67, pp. 335-40; for items in "Nature's Inventions" to *Audubon*, the magazine of the National Audubon Society; for the cartoon reprinted in "Take a Good Look" to Ed Orloff; and to Robert H. McKim for the transcription of his tape in "Become an Apple."

Special thanks are due to Catherine Hough for the drawings and illustrations that accompany some of the games and exercises.

Introduction

Creative Growth Games is a comprehensive training program for the full exploration and rapid enhancement of your creative powers.

Creative Growth Games will enable you to:

. . . discover new facets of your imagination and inventive powers that will help you cope with the chronic problems that weigh you down in your day-to-day living.

. . . think of many more alternative solutions to problems than the one—or perhaps two—you now use habitually.

. . . develop new modes and patterns of thought that will give you guidelines for working through your most perplexing problems and negative habit patterns—those downward spirals that take you deeper into familiar ruts.

One of the most persistent and widespread notions about creativity is that it is the exclusive province or preserve of only a few talented individuals. Unfortunately, many individuals admired for having this "mysterious" ability have been perfectly willing to perpetuate this notion of exclusivity. Consequently, people who think they lack creative ability tend either to overvalue it as an unattainable, almost magical attribute, a fancy, exalted talent; or they devalue and dismiss it as an impractical and frivolous luxury. Many people—especially in business and industry—even fear its disruptive influence. Apparently, old prejudices built on false assumptions still persist.

3

This damaging and inhibiting misinformation about creativity must now be discarded. An impressive body of solid research over the past few decades has conclusively proved that most of us were born with rich and vigorous imaginations, and that creative ability is almost universally distributed. There is also ample proof that creativity can be rekindled in those who seem to have lost it, or whose potential creativity is buried under layers of personal and environmental barriers and stiflers.

In addition, many creativity training programs have abundantly demonstrated that creative problem solving techniques and creative habits of mind can be learned, strengthened, enhanced, and effectively applied in daily living. Most of us have plenty of creative potential bottled up inside, waiting to get out into the daylight.

You Were Born Creative

In an important sense, creativity is contingent upon the preservation of the curiosity and sense of wonder we had in early childhood. Unfortunately, however, it is the one thing that is conspicuous by its absence in most grown-ups. Almost from the first grade on—and sometimes earlier—we are compelled to conform to a system which progressively constricts our freedom to imagine and to create new ideas. The erosion of our inborn creativity begins early and continues throughout our lives. While ostensibly preparing us for responsible adulthood, the enculturation and maturing processes most of us go through manage to conventionalize us to a degree where creative curiosity and wonder almost cease to exist. It is this that probably prompted the famous French psychologist, Jean Piaget, to state recently: "If you want to be creative, stay in part a child, with the creativity and invention that characterizes children before they are deformed by adult society."

Perhaps as a consequence of conformity pressures, there is among many adults a basic distrust of original thinking and fantasy making. We are conditioned and programmed by our soci-

4

ety to be intensely judgmental. We are often trigger-ready to attack new ideas the minute we hear them and to criticize thoughts that appear to have little or no factual underpinning. Ideas that do not conform to an accepted system are dismissed hastily. There is little doubt that this attitude has contributed to the observation that most adults in our society are mere "walking negative automatons." As you will later discover in this book, the key change you have to accomplish in your attitudes when thinking up creative ideas as possible solutions to your problems is to defer judgment or evaluation of the ideas as you conceive them.

The fascination of wonder and curiosity—qualities lost to many adults—are present in most children. They are directly related to the life-affirming attributes of creative responsiveness, aliveness, and growth. Anyone who has observed children closely has noticed that they have a heightened, strong sensitivity and awareness of the world around them. They have a spontaneous curiosity toward everything they touch or come in contact with during most of their waking moments. There is a precious propulsion toward seeking understanding, toward piercing the mystery they sense in everything they see.

Children also know the value of discovery. In their daily exploration, they repeatedly stumble upon—or perceive—new relationships among seemingly unrelated things, and once they have discovered these relationships, they never seem to tire of reviewing them. And this finding and seeing of relationships—especially between apparently unrelated things—is one of our most potent tools for unlocking creativity.

Children are capable of reacting spontaneously and interestedly to impressions, and they show an unqualified acceptance of fantasy and its workings. The rapt sense of wonder—the securest possession of almost every child—and the avid concern with the minutest details concerning their surroundings—in short, the sheer poetic intensity of living—is gone sooner than are all the other characteristics of childhood.

Most of us remember very little of what happened to us in early childhood, recovering perhaps only a few salient incidents. What we do vaguely recall, however, is the impression of having perceived the world in a different way. We may recall how rich and colorful everything was, how much mystery and surprise every new day brought with it, and how eagerly we fed on this experience. With age, however, the hues gradually dim and the mystery runs dry; the colors gradually dull to various shades of gray. With the passage of time, most adults lose their capacity and urge to wonder, to be surprised or puzzled. Their imaginations become constricted and their ability to see new relationships among phenomena becomes atrophied.

It is only in dreams that most adults occasionally escape the dreary gray and recapture the Technicolor of childhood. Only in dreams do they show that they can be courageously and uninhibitedly imaginative. During waking hours, on the other hand, the capacity to seek and to make discoveries, to imagine courageously and vividly, and to experience things that are outside the pale of everyday, narrow reality, is lost. It is indeed one of life's major tragedies that, for most people, the experience of dreaming, or the rare half-awake states of reverie, or the twilight of mood that music or beauty of nature evoke, are the few and rare excursions away from the coercive, problem-infested daily reality and the fetters of habit-existence. They are the seldom-traveled escape routes into the fairy-never-never-land of free and scaling imagination and its display of fireworks that life held constantly in youth.

Fortunately, our latent creativity really never becomes lost completely, only submerged under layers and layers of nonproductive habits and blocks. Through the process of unlearning these habits and then retraining ourselves to unstifle our creativity we can unearth our hidden potentials, bring them to the surface again, and make use of them for a more creative and fulfilling life. We can recapture and learn to have a keener sensitivity and awareness of the world around us, the world we live and work in.

Why Cultivate Creativity?

Apart from the sense of personal satisfaction that restoration of full functioning always brings, there are other important benefits to be gained.

There has scarcely been a time when we were as insecure as we are today. The insecurity that bothers us is not only outside, it is also within ourselves. It is part of us. A good deal of this insecurity can be attributed to the accelerating rate of change and the complexities we sense all around us. Today almost everyone is facing an increasing number of problems that did not even exist a few years ago, and every year this "problem escalation" seems to be increasing and intensifying.

As the saying "Nothing is permanent, except change" indicates, change is a constant in our universe. We might even say that change is natural, sameness unnatural. Yet more and more people these days look on change with a considerable sense of anxiety and trepidation. They want things to go back to the way they were, or they try to recapture the "good old days." But excursions and escapes into the past offer, at best, only a temporary respite from the problem-infested present. Sooner or later we have to face reality squarely and come to grips with the problems that the changes are creating.

Passive adaptation to change, to the ever-shifting present, is not enough. To bring about desired change and to decelerate or forestall undesired change, we have to learn not only to cope with change, but to become active participants in the change process. Unless we assume responsibility for controlling, harnessing, directing, and influencing change, the ensuing problems might someday overwhelm us.

All forecasts for the years ahead point to a period of unprecedented rate of change. To cope with the pressures and to seize the opportunities such a period will present, we need to become more creatively flexible and imaginative. Thus the most important ingredient for facing the future confidently may well turn out to be creativity. Confidence—or a sense of security—can result only from the conviction or belief that we are going to be able to meet the challenges and solve the problems of the future without relying on someone else to solve them for us. And only creativity can give us this confidence.

With liberated creativity and imagination, we no longer need to be dragged along by changes. We can not only manage and direct change, but we can make changes to open up new advantages and opportunities for ourselves and for our best interests. Using our imaginations and our creative talents to discover alternatives is one of the main ingredients in the management and making of change for the present, as well as for the future. The deeper we can dig into the vast reservoir of our latent creativity and make effective use of what we find there, the better we can manage and direct change for a more fulfilled existence for ourselves.

No one needs to experience life as a rat race in a maze, or a game in which the rules seem to be constantly changed. The potential human capacity for creative thought and action can literally make all the difference in the world. The real success stories in life are made by men and women who aren't afraid of trying new things, or looking at the problems around them from entirely new vantage points. It is surely a tragedy that most people continue, day after day, to flail away at their problems with conventional sweat, rather than creative sense.

But creativity has other enormous benefits. Although by no means complete, research has revealed that creativity:

Increases your sensitivity to problems, needs and opportunities, and your power to observe and perceive with more wide-awake attention. It helps you to look at things from new and different angles. It helps you to build a bridge beyond mere observation to seek deeper insights. When you see anything from a different point of view, you are breaking out of habitual behavior patterns and you are escaping from the treadmill of old ideas.

Enables you to discard old programs, old attitudes, and habitual ways of doing things that are no longer appropriate. It helps you to get rid of stereotyped and categorized thinking.

Releases you from mental rigidity and the staleness of routine and habit. It helps you to think beyond the cut-and-dried, the safe and sure, the tried and tested. It will make you dissatisfied with conventional thinking and the dubious comfort it temporarily provides.

Increases your capacity to search for new, different, and more effective ways to solve problems. It substantially improves your ability to get to the heart of your problems and to think up good ideas to solve them.

Enables you to multiply your alternatives and to make choices that enhance and nourish, rather than deplete you. It broadens the scope of your life.

Helps you to become more self-reliant, more self-trusting, and better able to mobilize your own resources. It enables you to extend, expand, develop, and express your capacities and your true potential.

Helps you to develop a new spirit of exploration and adventure—an awareness of the excitement and challenge in life. It increases your curiosity, enthusiasm, and the appetite for rewarding new experiences.

Prods you to keep thinking ahead and projecting your thoughts into the future instead of habitually and timidly looking backward at what worked and what didn't work.

Reawakens your spirit of experimentation and play. It helps you to recapture vitality, freshness, and the sense of wonder.

Gives you a sense of accomplishment, well-being, and purpose. It will make your work easier, more interesting, and more successful.

Creative Growth Games

Any dominant human power, whether it be muscular or mental, can be increased and revitalized by exercise. This is particularly true of the mental powers of creativity and imagination. No matter how unused and dormant they are, they can be revitalized through exercise. In fact, imagination and creativity *thrive* on exercise; without it, they wither. And it is just such a series of exercises that this book provides.

The book is a learning program specifically designed to:

1. Revitalize, develop, and strengthen in you all the important components or attributes of creative behavior and innovative problem solving, and

2. Give you repeated insights into the kinds of difficulties you face as a problem solver, and how they can be overcome.

This two-pronged approach will give you immediate rewards if you give the games and exercises your full attention. As you stimulate and develop your creative powers, as you free your creative imagination by reducing and overcoming the blocks and barriers to creative thinking that may have hampered and inhibited you for so long, you will observe a dramatic increase in your ability to solve concrete problems in your daily life. You'll be amazed at how quickly you will be able to look at your problems with fresh eyes, avoiding counterproductive routines and seemingly comfortable "nowhere" ruts. You will develop an attitude of readiness to consider something new, instead of always stubbornly clinging to the old.

When you combine your freed resources and your liberated creative energies with the habit of tackling your life's problems creatively, there will be virtually no limit to the ever-widening areas in which you can use your constructive imagination. You can live a more creative life-style, tackle more and more adventurous projects, and bring your achievements to unprecedented new heights.

Using your imagination is very enjoyable and exciting, and we think you will find *Creative Growth Games* great fun to do. With many of you they will grow into a new, more productive way of life. These games and exercises will activate and stimulate your imagination. You will learn with each one of them effective, new techniques; you will learn how to inhibit the inhibitors of your imagination and overcome the roadblocks to a more productive use of your talents.

> *I listen and forget,*
> *I read and understand,*
> *I see and remember,*
> *I do and I learn.*
> —*Oriental proverb*

The Best Approach

A few general observations about how to use this book to your best advantage are in order. First, it is *not* a book to be raced through to see how it comes out. How it comes out depends in large measure on what you put into it.

Although some of the games and exercises are in the form of problems or puzzles, most do not have one single "right" answer. And all are there to demonstrate an important point that you may well want to ponder before going on to the next challenge. The games and exercises cumulatively enhance your creative powers and enrich the vigor of your imagination.

Second, try your best not to get too "ego involved" or discouraged with the games and exercises. No one but you will ever know how many you solved or failed to solve, or how many mistakes you made. In learning to master creative problem-solving, many times the best way—and sometimes the only way—to learn is through mistakes. In fact, fear of making mistakes is one of the most inhibiting attitudes to effective problem-solving. The fear of being caught in an error and being thought less of because of it, can transform a potentially creative person into an unthinking robot.

As we grow older, our fear of making mistakes seems to increase. As a result, we stay close to the safe, but frequently trite and nonproductive paths of habitual behavior. Actually, mistakes can be considered invaluable stepping-stones to more effective living *if* we are willing to learn from them. With the new understanding that mistakes teach us, we can create a useful reference book of knowledge, one of inestimable value for meeting future challenges with greater confidence. Paraphrasing George Santayana, those who don't learn from their mistakes are compelled to repeat them.

The Creative Growth Games are *not* to be considered as so many individual "tests" or yardsticks against which you are measured, or measure yourself. They are there only to enhance your creative problem solving skills. Each game or exercise is designed to expose you to a new way of thinking, to a new thought model, and to provide instant feedback on how well you are doing.

The four tests at regular intervals have been provided to prove to you that you have made progress, and that further improvement and growth are possible as you proceed further with the games and exercises. If the games and exercises are conscientiously done, you will see an improvement of at least 30 percent, and perhaps as much as 300 percent in your creative problem solving ability. This book gives you a self-training program that you can approach at your own pace, whenever and wherever you like.

Creative Growth Games provides you with repeated and continuous stimulation and reinforcement for your creative thinking. They will help you to reach inside yourself to release your latent and untapped creativity within. But remember: the entire process of learning a more creative behavior, and of developing a more creative life-style depends on you yourself. What you will get out of this book depends on the time and effort you will put into it. The creative urge, the creative capability is inherent in all of us. Nurtured and practiced, it expands as we grow; stifled or even left alone, it contracts.

By practice and effort, we do not mean drudgery. Personal growth and self-discovery constitute one of the most rewarding undertakings available to anyone. In an important sense, it is the unfolding of wonder and richness in ourselves—an inward journey that never ceases to be fascinating. *Creative Growth Games* will certainly stimulate and enhance your voyage of self-discovery.

It is now widely recognized that creativity is vital to an individual's psychological health. There is a reciprocal and cyclical relationship between a person's mental health and his creative expression: whatever enhances his creativity promotes his psychological health; and whatever improves his psychological health increases his creativity.

Both creativity and psychological health can be described in terms that belong to the same family of meanings. They are both associated with integration, wholeness, commitment, unity, self-fulfillment, authenticity, goal direction, vitality, enthusiasm, personal involvement, deeper self-realization, high motivation, greater self-knowledge, and positive action.

At the turn of the century, the philosopher William James observed that normal, healthy, productive people function at 10 percent or less of their capacity. In 1966 anthropologist Margaret Mead placed it at 6 percent, and the most recent estimate by the humanistic psychologist Herbert Otto is closer to 4 percent. It is clear that we *all* use only a fraction of our potential, and that we've all got a long way to go.

Creative Growth Games will have done its job if it convinces you that, whatever your age, background or educational level, further creative growth in your personal and professional life is both possible and pleasurable. It is likely that the mental dexterity you will derive from **Creative Growth Games** and the stimulus it provides your mind will not be equalled by any other pursuit or training in which you will engage.

As you apply your newly won creative powers, you will find you'll have fewer unsolved problems—and this, in turn, will contribute greatly to your peace of mind and your joy of living. You will discover that you've become a permanent part of something rare and wonderful, and that your future can be an exciting and novel place, a better, more meaningful place, and a happier place.

Eugene Raudsepp
George P. Hough, Jr.
Princeton Creative Research, Inc.
Princeton, N. J.

PRE-TEST: WOODEN BLOCKS

The pre-test and three other tests in this book are presented to show the impact the games and exercises will have on your creative problem solving ability. It is therefore advisable that you take the pre-test *now*, before proceeding with the games and exercises. You will need only a paper and a pencil.

IN EXACTLY FIVE (5) MINUTES, LIST ALL POSSIBLE USES FOR A *WOODEN BLOCK* OR *BLOCKS* (ANY SIZE).

PART I: GAMES AND EXERCISES

Through the process of association of ideas your imagination will find new and relevant relationships between things.

Creativity is contagious, pass it on.

#1: KINDRED RELATIONS

There have been—and continue to be—many efforts to define or explain the creation process. Dr. Sarnoff A. Mednick of the University of Michigan, a psychologist, thinks of it as the forming of associative elements into new combinations or arrangements.

That may not be the whole story, but certainly the person who can marshal a great number of associations and ideas and bring them to bear on his problem has a better chance of coming up with a satisfying and original solution than has a person who produces few associations and ideas.

This exercise can help your creative thinking enormously. Take all the time you can to complete it.

This exercise is a natural for a party game, but choose partners who are articulate and who possess a large vocabulary.

THINK OF A FIFTH WORD THAT IS RELATED TO THE PRECEDING FOUR WORDS. (YOU CAN FORM COMPOUNDS, HYPHENATED WORDS IN SOME CASES, OR COMMONLY USED EXPRESSIONS).

Examples:

1. Elephant, bleed, lie, wash _____
   Answer: White (white elephant, bleed white, white lie, whitewash)
2. Sleeping, contest, spot, shop _____
   Answer: Beauty (sleeping beauty, beauty contest, beauty spot, beauty shop)
3. Style, love, jacket, span _____
   Answer: Life (life-style, love life, life jacket, life span)
4. Opera, fly, feathers, laugh _____
   Answer: Horse (horse opera, horsefly, horsefeathers, horse-laugh)
5. Iron, Latin, pen, skin _____
   Answer: Pig (pig iron, pig Latin, pigpen, pigskin)

Now train your own associative powers with the following sets:

1. BUG	REST	FELLOW	COVER	___
2. CROSS	BABY	BLOOD	RIBBON	___
3. SEE	CARPET	HOT	CENT	___
4. TOUCH	PALATE	SOAP	SELL	___
5. EASY	HUSH	BELT	ORDER	___
6. TREE	CUP	CAKE	FORBIDDEN	___
7. WAGON	STAND	AID	DANCE	___
8. DUST	MOVIE	GAZE	SAPPHIRE	___
9. TOOTH	TALK	POTATO	BITTER	___
10. ALLEY	DATE	SNOW	SPOT	___
11. CALL	NAP	BURGLER	HEP	___
12. REST	POST	LINEN	FELLOW	___
13. BULLDOG	CUFF	TOAST	WINDOWS	___
14. OPERA	NO	BOX	STONE	___
15. BRAIN	WATCHING	BATH	HOUSE	___

16. WIRE	OUT	FEED	PLAY	_____
17. STUDIES	WORK	SCIENCE	WELFARE	_____
18. STORAGE	SHOULDER	COMFORT	CREAM	_____
19. WALK	NEW	SCAPE	BEAM	_____
20. BUSINESS	SUIT	WRENCH	SHINE	_____
21. FIRE	HOLE	BENT	CATCH	_____
22. DAYS	BISCUIT	COLLAR	EAR	_____
23. CLAY	BREAST	ENGLISH	HEARTED	_____
24. PLAY	BREAST	POX	WIRE	_____
25. BELT	MAGIC	MARKET	HEAD	_____
26. GUY	CRACK	UP	MAN	_____
27. MOUTH	SHOT	STICK	TIME	_____
28. DIRTY	CYCLE	OFFICE	SCHOOL	_____
29. BEATER	HEAD	ROLL	ROTTEN	_____
30. DRESS	MUSICAL	STAR	PRAYER	_____
31. HUNTER	LIGHT	WIND	STAND	_____
32. ACTOR	WITNESS	SKETCH	ODD	_____
33. SHAVE	QUARTERS	CALL	DOWN	_____
34. BELLY	FEVER	JOURNALISM	PAGES	_____
35. A	B	C	E	_____
36. AWAY	POST	BOARD	LANGUAGE	_____
37. STAR	GLORY	AFTER	SICKNESS	_____
38. SEAT	SUIT	BROAD	BAIL	_____
39. BOY	BELL	HAND	HIDE	_____
40. SURE	CROW	EYED	FIGHT	_____
41. AGE	CLASS	BROW	EAR	_____
42. FRENCH	TAKING	ALONE	ON	_____

Productivity is desirable, creativity more so.

Almost all creativity involves purposive play.

#2: CONCEALED COLORS

This game is designed to increase your flexibility and your ability to overcome the restrictions of habit.

Play it with friends. The one who can identify most of the "hidden colors" first, is the winner.

THE NAME OF WHAT COLOR IS CONCEALED IN EACH SENTENCE?

Examples:
1. Newspaper editors decided to go on strike.
   Answer: Red.
2. The cab lacked proper brakes to stop at the intersection.
   Answer: Black.

Now try these:
1. A big, old, hungry dog appeared at our door every morning.
2. The cop persuaded him not to create a disturbance.
3. The Brazilian student Paulo lives just around the corner from us.
4. You shouldn't let an upstart like him bother you.
5. He let out a big yell, owing to the injuries he received when he fell.
6. La Jolla venders decided to cut their prices in half.
7. Long rayon fabrics were loaded on the truck.
8. The Austrian physicist Wolfgang Pauli lacked the requisite documents to enter the United States.
9. You shouldn't sell this fossil very cheaply because it is a rare specimen.

10. The new law hit everybody's pocketbook pretty hard.
11. The kitten chased the big pear lying near the tree.
12. You can always catch Rome on your way back from Naples.
13. No one thought of awnings to protect the merchandise from the sun.
14. After you wipe the sweat off your brow, nestle a little closer to me.
15. To build up your chest, nutrients derived from milk products are the best.
16. Bob's car let out dark fumes when he tried to drive it up the steep hill.
17. The famous composer Ernest Bloch resumed conducting the orchestra after a brief intermission.
18. He decided to leap, in keeping with the agreement reached with the referee.
19. The old ogre entered the argument with obvious relish.
20. A huge dog called Lobo ran gently toward me.
21. After you've let the cat in, dig out the buried treasure.

Imagination is the laboratory wherein are developed the ideas of man.

We only use a small fraction of our inherent creative potential.

#3: TELL A STORY

Many of us have no trouble in spontaneously creating stories to amuse small children—probably because we know that children will accept unlikely plots without criticism. But outside of this context, we may be inhibited about "story telling." Fluency of imagination is easily inhibited, but it is all-important and needs to be exercised.

This exercise is designed to strengthen and free your imaginative powers and keep your fantasy moving.

It can be great fun when played with others. Use it as an excuse to have a stimulating party. Choose game partners who enjoy using their imaginations.

VIVIDLY IMAGINE THE GIVEN OBJECTS IN FRONT OF YOU. THEN WRITE A STORY ABOUT WHAT YOU SEE IN YOUR MIND'S EYE, USING AS GUIDES THESE THREE QUESTIONS:

1. WHAT PRECEDED OR LED UP TO THIS?
2. WHAT IS GOING ON NOW?
3. WHAT COULD THE OUTCOME BE?

BE SURE TO USE *ALL* THESE THREE QUESTIONS.
OBJECTS: *A BROKEN CANE. A BROKEN CRUTCH.*

Education for living is best accomplished by exercising creativity.

The mainspring of creativity is curiosity.

#4: THE FRUGAL WOMAN

Successful problem-solvers are able to think of many different explanations for the things they observe. Only after they have amassed as many explanations as they can, do they subject them to test or critical analysis to arrive at the best or most likely explanation.

Less creative problem-solvers tend to be mentally impatient. They hug to their bosoms the first likely explanation that occurs to them and rest content with it. The generation of hypotheses—

or ideas—is a crucial part of problem analysis for the simple reason that we can't evaluate an explanation that hasn't occurred to us.

This exercise makes another good rainy-day party game.

A WOMAN CHANGES HER FRUGAL HABITS AND SPENDS MONEY VERY FREELY. HOW MANY PRIOR CIRCUMSTANCES CAN YOU SUGGEST TO ACCOUNT FOR THIS? LIST AS MANY IDEAS AS YOU CAN.

To put more zest into your life, try creativity.

Many problems remain unsolved because people look for solutions, and not for new ways of viewing the problems.

#5: LOOSE ENDS

This problem illustrates how defining a problem too narrowly can inhibit and delay finding a solution.

The successful problem-solver tries to state the requirements as broadly as possible at the beginning. If after a reasonable time, no solution presents itself, he suspects that the problem needs redefinition. He then tries to restate it in such a way that a new avenue of approach becomes available.

Less successful problem-solvers, on the other hand, persist doggedly in the same direction, even when the difficulty does not yield to their efforts. They are blocked from considering new directions by stubborn commitment to the old.

Look at the sketch below and imagine that you are the person shown standing in this room. You have been given the task of tying together the ends of the two strings suspended from the ceiling. The strings are located so that you cannot reach one string with your outstretched hand while holding the second in your hand. The room is totally bare, and you have only the resources you would normally have in your pocket or handbag. How do you solve this problem?

A mind that has no imaginative outlet is like a house without windows.

In the creative mind, new insights wink on and off like fireflies.

#6: SHORT SUCCINCT SENTENCES

Most of us are trained and learn to write in purely practical ways. We are concerned only with the content of our communications and are hardly aware of the sounds we are making. However, those individuals who create society's enduring poetry and prose listen to the sounds as well as the sense of words. Being able to voluntarily let go of sense for a moment and let words come as they will is one key to improving writing and thinking skills. This exercise gives practice in "reaching for sounds" in the same way that punning does.

WRITE THREE-WORD PHRASES BEGINNING WITH:
    THE LETTER B.
Example: Buy better bargains.
    THE LETTER T.
Example: Telling tall tales
    For each letter, write as many phrases as you can in five minutes.

> *Think up more ideas than you can use.*
>
> *Generate lots of ideas before you evaluate them, there is always plenty of time to separate the chaff from the grain.*

#7: SAFETY DRIVE

One of the best techniques to help you in creative problem-solving and solution finding is "brainstorming"—widely used in business and industry. It can be used either by groups or individuals, and the rules are few and simple:

1. *Quantity* of ideas is the goal, not quality.
2. No judgment or evaluation may take place until all the ideas are in.
3. Unusual or fanciful ideas are encouraged.
4. Where a group is involved, members are encouraged to "piggyback" on other's ideas, adding features or variations.

Get your friends to join you when doing this exercise. You'll be surprised and intrigued by both the quantity and the quality of possibilities and ideas that will be produced.

Don't be afraid of being farfetched or silly—these are frequently signs that you've overcome the inhibitions that hamper your creative mind.

LET'S ASSUME THAT IT BECAME IMPERATIVE TO REDUCE AUTOMOBILE ACCIDENTS BY ANY AND ALL MEANS POSSIBLE. HOW MIGHT IT BE DONE? GIVE YOURSELF TEN MINUTES TO PRODUCE AT LEAST TWENTY SUGGESTIONS.

Humor provides the therapeutic jolt that shifts things into their proper perspective.

You have to relax and have fun to be creative. You can't do it when you're too serious.

#8: TAKE A GOOD LOOK

The humor of cartoons and other "visual jokes" depends heavily on exaggeration, or hyperbole—clearly the case with the example shown. The drawing conveys a physical impossibility which is nonetheless laughable because it echoes an experience or feeling with which we are all familiar. We've all been asked more than once to "open a little wider, please."

WRITE SEVERAL CAPTIONS FOR THIS CARTOON.

Thinking in terms of absolutes freezes creativity; thinking in terms of relativity frees it.

The rut of habit is a grave without end.

#9: MEDICAL EMERGENCY

Stereotyped thinking is one of the major barriers to creative problem solving. The impulse to overgeneralize about human beings is one most of us never fully conquer. But it is worth struggling with, because it can grossly mislead us—as this little puzzle illustrates.

A young man, badly injured in an auto accident, is brought into the emergency room of a hospital. It is determined by the attending physician that immediate brain surgery is required. Accordingly, the brain surgeon is summoned. Upon seeing the patient, the surgeon exclaims, "My God, I can't operate on that boy! He's my son!"

That is so, but the surgeon is not the boy's father. How do you explain the apparent contradiction?

The arrogance of logic obstructs the use of new ideas.

We are passing beyond the era of the intelligent person, and a new one is dawning: the age of the creative person.

#10: DIAMONDS AND RUBIES

This exercise illustrates the important difference between what Edward de Bono calls *vertical* and *lateral* thinking.

Vertical thinking is traditional logical thinking in which you proceed in an orderly manner from point to point, supporting each step on the preceding one. But vertical thinking is not of much help in solving many real-life problems because it leads you to only a limited number—and frequently ineffective—alternate solutions.

Lateral thinking, on the other hand, frees your mind to consider many alternatives, not constrained by any logical framework. It helps you to make deliberate jumps in your thinking and to avoid being hemmed in by customary ideas and old boundaries. With lateral thinking you can change horses in midstream, change your direction, and open your mind to the intrusion of chance ideas.

With this in mind, try to solve the following problem. Get others to join you in this mind-expanding exercise.

Once upon a time, there lived a widowed queen who had a beautiful daughter. Along came a prince who fell deeply in love with her. The princess shared his feelings and they decided to ask the queen for permission to marry.

The queen, a selfish, ugly, and jealous woman, also fancied the young prince and wanted to make him her own. The queen was so rich that her garden path was littered with diamonds and rubies, and she was willing to give all her riches to the prince if he would only consent to marry her. The prince refused and insisted that he only wanted the princess.

One day while the three of them were walking on the garden path, the queen proposed that they let chance decide the matter. She told them that she would put a diamond and a ruby into an empty jewelry box and then the princess would have to pick out one of the precious stones without looking. If she picked the ruby, the prince would marry the queen; if she picked the diamond, she would be free to marry the prince.

Reluctantly, the young prince and princess decided to accept the gamble. The queen stooped down to pick up the two stones. As she picked up the stones, the princess noticed that the sly old queen picked up two rubies, instead of a diamond and a ruby, and put them into the jewelry box. She then ordered the princess to pick out the stone that was to decide the marriage arrangement.

*To do creative thinking, you have to
allow your mind to freewheel.*

*You cannot do everything at once, you
have to take it one step at a time.*

#12: BRIDGE THE GAPS

Most of us hamper our creative thinking by letting our vocabularies become rigid and frozen. This exercise will enable you to attain greater freedom and fluency in your vocabulary. It will also loosen up your mind to form quick associations. And associations are the stuff from which new concepts and original ideas are made.

Playing it with others makes it an interesting game to stimulate imagination.

FILL IN EACH OF THE THREE SPACES BETWEEN THE TWO "KEY WORDS" WITH WORDS WHICH HAVE A MEANINGFUL RELATION WITH THE WORD PRECEDING AND FOLLOWING IT.

Examples:

1. Dark _____ _____ _____ shovel
   Possible Answers: Dark color white snow shovel
2. School _____ _____ _____ run
   Possible answers: School guard house dog run

Now it's your turn:

1. Star _____ _____ _____ before
2. Lemon _____ _____ _____ dog
3. Fire _____ _____ _____ scared
4. Dog _____ _____ _____ white
5. Postage _____ _____ _____ knee
6. White _____ _____ _____ about
7. Short _____ _____ _____ out

29

8. Blood	_____	_____	_____	color
9. Light	_____	_____	_____	test
10. Blue	_____	_____	_____	ball
11. Hunt	_____	_____	_____	house
12. Cat	_____	_____	_____	car
13. Sleep	_____	_____	_____	bad
14. Concert	_____	_____	_____	machine
15. Puppy	_____	_____	_____	home

Man masters reality through his creative imagination.

Your imagination cannot work in a vacuum; it must have something to work on, something upon which it can concentrate its force.

#13: THE MIND'S EYE

Chances are you've already played this game: Fold a piece of paper, drop some ink in the crease, then press the folded paper flat to get strange symmetrical patterns.

Hermann Rorschach, the famous Swiss psychologist, developed this into one of the most widely used and highly respected personality tests. While in the original Rorschach test the forms or "blots" are symmetrical, and several in color, these are black and asymmetrical, to give your imagination more of a workout.

As you "project" yourself into the designs that follow, make a special effort to focus on the shapes as a whole. You may turn them in any direction, to change orientation, or view them at any distance by propping the open book on some convenient surface. Take your time and try for the most complete and detailed responses you can produce. Give as many descriptions of the patterns as you can. What shapes, objects, or even scenes, do you see?

The creative person spends more time in formulating, analyzing, and organizing his problem before attempting solution; the less creative person wants to "get on with it."

Sometimes a problem is a problem only because it is looked at from only one angle; looked at from another, the solution becomes so obvious that the problem no longer exists.

#14: SIMPLE ARITHMETIC

This exercise is one of the few in this book that you have to do against a time limit. Creative thinking isn't usually done best within specified time limits, but our hurried environment frequently imposes this restriction. See if you can find a way to beat this problem before you tackle it. Sometimes you have to be able to step back to see what's involved.

IN THE FOLLOWING SIMPLE ARITHMETIC PROBLEMS: PLUS (+) SIGN MEANS TO MULTIPLY; DIVIDE (÷) SIGN MEANS TO ADD; MINUS (-) SIGN MEANS TO DIVIDE; TIMES (X) SIGN MEANS TO SUBTRACT. SEE HOW MANY PROBLEMS YOU CAN COMPLETE IN EXACTLY *ONE* MINUTE.

7 + 2	8 ÷ 4	6 + 5	8 ÷ 4	6 + 11
20 - 10	7 X 7	9 + 3	5 X 2	8 - 4
9 ÷ 3	2 ÷ 2	8 ÷ 4	6 + 6	9 + 2
12 X 2	15 - 5	4 X 3	20 + 2	20 - 10
6 X 5	15 - 3	16 ÷ 8	15 ÷ 5	5 ÷ 5
10 + 2	7 X 5	9 X 2	10 - 5	5 ÷ 1
10 ÷ 10	8 ÷ 2	4 X 2	8 + 3	10 - 2
4 - 2	15 - 3	9 ÷ 3	16 X 6	8 ÷ 8

*You can reawaken your creative habit
and strengthen it through exercise.*

*If you want to be creative, you have to
have ideas to play around with.*

#15: MAKE SOMETHING OF IT

This exercise will flex and liberate your visual imagination. It
has nothing to do with drawing skill. There is no "right answer," nor is there any "hidden picture" to find.

TURN THE FOLLOWING TWO SKETCHES INTO
SOMETHING RECOGNIZABLE.

To complete these unfinished drawings, you may turn them
into any position you want. Use the lines and curves to form a
logical part of the picture you produce. And again, don't worry
about "not being able to draw."

This game is another good one to play with others. Everybody's drawing is evaluated and judged by others. Give five
points for a very original and intriguing sketch, all the way
down to one point for something that is obvious and lacking in
imagination.

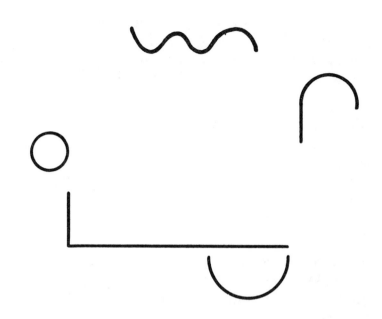

We can never truly know what we are not aware of, and only creativity can bring us new awareness.

True understanding comes only through creativity.

#16: BRIGHT BUT SHY

Several psychological experiments have shown that the noncreative, or less creative people—when exposed to a paradoxical or problematic situation—tend to rest content with only the one or two explanations they can think of. On the other hand, the more creative individuals spend more time analyzing a situation and scanning a broad range of alternatives. They are apt to think of as many alternative explanations as they can, and only then will they narrow their long list down to the more plausible or reasonable explanations.

Taking a look into what causes a particular situation requires using creative imagination. You can practice this exercise with friends. You're apt to have an insight-expanding discussion and a lot of fun.

Here is a statement which may, or may not be, true, but which you are to *assume* is true or valid. Give as many plausible or reasonable explanations as you can to explain the "truth" of this statement:

IT HAS BEEN FOUND THAT BRIGHTER INDIVIDUALS SUFFER MORE FROM FEELINGS OF INADEQUACY AND INFERIORITY THAN DO THE LESS BRIGHT INDIVIDUALS.

> *Identifying the problem is half the battle.*
>
> *Most of us try to solve problems by habit and fool ourselves into thinking that we have really solved them—when in fact, we haven't.*

#17: THE COLLECTED WORKS

We are frequently hampered in creative problem-solving by our habitual ways of looking at things. The more familiar a situation or an object is, the harder it is to see it differently. Creativity, however, requires a "fresh pair of eyes."

While this problem looks deceptively simple, it is actually quite difficult. As a matter of fact, only about one person in a hundred is able to solve it the first time around. The problem is included because it is extremely instructive.

THERE ARE FOUR VOLUMES OF SHAKESPEARE'S COLLECTED WORKS ON THE SHELF:

THE PAGES OF EACH VOLUME ARE EXACTLY 2" THICK. THE COVERS ARE EACH 1/6" THICK. THE BOOKWORM STARTED EATING AT PAGE I OF VOLUME I AND IT ATE THROUGH TO THE LAST PAGE OF VOLUME IV. WHAT IS THE DISTANCE THE BOOKWORM COVERED?

One creative thought triggers others.

When you fail to use your creative ability,
you diminish the quality of your life.

#18: MANY MEANINGS

Many kinds of creative endeavor depend on words. Writers, copywriters, poets, speakers, and editors are among those who manipulate verbal symbols for a living.

The ability to make accurate verbal distinctions—to know lots of words and how they are similar and different—is very important both in thinking and writing. In fact, poverty of language is almost always accompanied by poverty of thought. But this ability to use a rich array of words and synonyms is not inborn. It can be taught, and even self-taught.

This exercise will increase your fluency to think up a quantity of words and phrases that belong to the same family of meanings. And this "family" has many members.

LIST AS MANY WORDS AND PHRASES AS YOU CAN THAT MEAN THE SAME—OR ALMOST THE SAME—AS THE WORD *CLEVER* (BOTH ITS POSITIVE AND NEGATIVE MEANINGS).

In a rapidly changing world, creativity is
a priceless asset.

When you use your imagination, you're
free to do the utmost with your mind—no
holds barred.

#19: WHAT WOULD HAPPEN IF—I

This old parlor game, where the task is to think of the possible consequences of certain unusual happenings, is one of the most valuable exercises to "loosen up" your imagination. It develops your resourcefulness and encourages you to think beyond the commonplace, the stereotyped, and the habitual. When applied to our everyday problems, the "what would happen if attitude" helps you to view them from new and fresh angles.

Example:

What would happen if we also had two eyes in the back of our heads?

Possible answers:

1. We could accomplish more by being able to attend to more things at the same time; e.g., read and write simultaneously.
2. Cars would not have to have rear-window mirrors, and accidents would decrease.
3. Mugging and other crimes would decrease; nobody would be able to sneak up behind one's back.
4. All hats would have brims front and back.
5. Eyeglasses would be completely redesigned.
6. Opticians would have twice as much business.
7. New hairstyles would have to be created which would not cover up the eyes.
8. Cheating at examinations would be virtually stopped because the teacher would be able to survey the entire classroom all the time.
9. Movie theaters would be redesigned to show films on opposite walls.
10. People would never collide on the dance floor.
11. On opening night, the producer of a play would be able to see the performance on the stage and at the same time measure audience reaction.
12. Men wouldn't have to turn around to ogle pretty girls they just passed.

Play this game with friends. Use it as a contest for who produces the greatest number of alternative answers, as well as the most original responses.

WHAT WOULD HAPPEN IF PEOPLE COULD MARRY AS MANY PEOPLE AS THEY WANTED TO?

When you refuse to accept the obvious, you've taken your first giant step toward creativity.

Directions are rules that can be changed.

#20: HALF OF THIRTEEN

This is an exercise in ingenuity and persistence. It increases your ability to look at a problem from as many different angles or viewpoints as possible.

HOW MANY DIFFERENT ANSWERS CAN YOU THINK OF TO THE QUESTION: "WHAT IS HALF OF THIRTEEN?"

Of course, the obvious answer is 6.5. See if you can find other acceptable answers. This exercise is not easy, but don't be discouraged. Chances are you can stump your friends with it.

The creative person escapes one of life's major maladies: boredom.

In the creative adult, the pipeline to childhood remains uncluttered and direct.

#21: FUN WITH PUNS

Several recent psychological experiments have shown that humor, wit, and "playfulness" are directly related to creativity. One type of humor is the ability to pun.

Punning—the association by sound affinity—has manifested itself in diverse cultures and epochs, and is evident in poetry, in dreams, and in the punning mania of children.

MAKE UP A "PUN DEFINITION" FOR EACH OF THE FOLLOWING WORDS (NOT A STANDARD DICTIONARY DEFINITION). A "PUN DEFINITION" INVOLVES THE CHANGING OF THE PRONUNCIATION AND/OR THE MEANING OF PART(S) OF THE WORD. MAKE YOUR ANSWERS AS BRIEF AND CLEAR AS YOU CAN. (Some words lend themselves to several "pun definitions.")

Examples:

Bulldoze — a sleeping animal
Abuse — a motor vehicle (bus)
Jargon — glass container missing

Now try these:

ILLEGAL. PAROLE. HYDROPHOBIA. ARMATURE.
KIDNAP.   CURTAIL.   OVERTIRED.   THERAPIST.
KINDRED.   FEROCITY.

41

*Don't be·afraid of your ideas—they can
only help you.*

*An unexpected creative thought can make
all the difference in the world.*

#22: COME AS YOU ARE

While it is unlikely that you'll ever be caught in the following
situation, life presents us with many problems where creative
imagination can spell the difference between success and failure.

JUST BEFORE YOU HAVE TO GO TO AN IMPOR-
TANT EVENING PARTY, A SMALL FIRE BREAKS
OUT IN YOUR CLOTHES CLOSET. WHILE THE
DAMAGE IS NOT EXTENSIVE, ALL OF YOUR
CLOTHES ARE DESTROYED. WHAT WOULD YOU
DO TO BE ABLE TO ATTEND THE PARTY? LIST AS
MANY IDEAS AS YOU CAN.

*Once you are possessed by the creative
urge, all other drives recede into insignifi-
cance.*

*Bad-mouthing someone's new idea is a
counterfeit way of demonstrating your intellectual superiority.*

#23: SHORT DEFINITIONS

Someone once said, "There is not a thought in our heads which
hasn't been worn shiny by other brains." While this may be
true, it is also possible to deliberately train our ability to add
unique quality and flavor to our thoughts, and to our observations on life's experiences. This exercise was expressly designed
for this.

This is another stimulating game to play at a party where both men and women are present. Each definition is rated by all the other players as: witty and original—3 points, good and interesting—2 points, and acceptable but common—1 point. In addition to exercising imagination, this game will give you fresh new insights into your friends' personalities and values.

GIVE YOUR OWN ORIGINAL, WITTY DEFINITIONS (NOT DICTIONARY DEFINITIONS) OF THE FOLLOWING.

Example: A bore.
Possible definition: "A person who talks when you wish him to listen."

Now try these: 1. PATIENCE. 2. HOPE. 3. A PASTOR. 4. A POLITICIAN. 5. AN EXPERT. 6. A WEED. 7. A GRAPEFRUIT. 8. REVOLUTION.

> *The feeling of creative understanding is as private as loving, dying, or pain.*
>
> *Where creative thought is lacking, everything is lacking.*

#24: WHAT GOES DOWN, BUT WON'T GO UP?

Here is a classic "story" puzzle that may be familiar to you. Even if it is, and you *do* remember the logical, but rather offbeat solution, don't stop there. One of the hallmarks of creative behavior is the willingness to explore alternative solutions—rather than accepting the one that comes most easily to mind. Turn your imagination loose.

THE PUZZLE GOES LIKE THIS: A MAN LIVING ON THE TWENTY-SECOND FLOOR OF AN APARTMENT BUILDING TAKES THE AUTOMATIC ELEVATOR ALL THE WAY DOWN TO THE LOBBY, BUT HE DOES NOT TAKE IT ALL THE WAY UP. WHY? GIVE AS MANY POSSIBLE REASONS AS YOU CAN.

In creativity, what is done is not as important as how it is done.

Custom, familiarity, and rigid habits provide dubious comfort—a creative person resists their legacy.

#25: A WOMAN'S INGENUITY

With some problems, a creative solution can only occur after the elements or parts of the problem have been reorganized into a different pattern. This requires you to do some juggling of the parts visually, in your mind's eye. With this in mind, see if you can solve this problem.

A businessman brought back from Europe four pieces of chain in solid gold, each consisting of three links:

He wanted to keep these as an investment, but his wife felt
that joined together these pieces would make a lovely necklace.
So she went to a jeweler and said, "I want you to connect these
pieces to make a necklace. How much will it cost?" The jeweler
laid the individual pieces of chain out in this pattern:

He told her, "I charge $2.50 to break a link, and $2.50 to
solder it together again. Since you have four corners, it will cost
you $20." The lady said, "That's too much. Actually you can
do it for $15." The problem, then, is to construct a necklace,
breaking and joining only three links. How would you do it?

INTERMEDIATE TEST A: MONEY . . . MONEY . . . MONEY

IN EXACTLY FIVE (5) MINUTES, LIST ALL POSSIBLE USES FOR COINS (PENNIES, NICKELS, DIMES, QUARTERS, SILVER DOLLARS, ETC.).

The only way to survive in a world that is buffeted by change is through creativity and innovation.

The worst you can do with your ideas is to hoard them.

#26: HOW HEADLINES HAPPEN

This exercise resembles Exercise #6—*Short Succinct Sentences*—but imposes two additional restraints: that an additional word beginning with the same letter be found, and that it makes sense as a newspaper headline. That is, it must have a subject, a verb and either an adverb or an adjective.

In *An Introduction to Journalism*, F. Fraser Bond points out: "Although he works anonymously, the copyreader, when he constructs a good headline, joins the ranks of the creative artist." The headline writer has very narrow literary limits, constrained by type style, a certain measure or number of characters, and the need to both attract attention and state the story's main facts accurately. We've given you a break on some of these limits, but imposed another—that of alliteration.

WRITE FOUR-WORD "HEADLINES" BEGINNING WITH THE LETTER "S".

Examples: Storm Sweeps Southern Spain
Stolen Stradivarius Still Sought

*A person who never made a mistake
never tried anything new.*

*A life lived without fantasy is a seriously
impoverished life.*

#27: LEAD PARAGRAPH

Newspapers are written for people on the run. It is a time-honored convention of journalistic writing that the beginning or "lead paragraph" should always tell the main facts of the story, so that the hasty reader needs to go no further.

TAKE ONE OF THE "HEADLINES" YOU WROTE IN THE PRECEDING EXERCISE AND WRITE A "LEAD PARAGRAPH" THAT EXPLAINS WHAT IT'S ALL ABOUT, IN THE STYLE OF A TABLOID NEWSPAPER.

Look at your paragraph and see if you've included all the necessary information concerning who, what, when, where, why, and how. It's easy to overlook one of these basic bits of information and it's *not* so easy to write them briefly, yet gracefully.

Imagine that you are standing on the queen's garden path. What would you do if you were the unfortunate princess? What advice would you offer her?

You have to free yourself of rules, restrictions, and restraints, in order to make discoveries.

When you say something is impossible, you've abandoned the winners and joined the losers.

#11: BREAKING OUT

This classic puzzle shows how easy it is to read into a problem restrictions that don't exist. Most of us impose too many imaginary boundaries, restrictions, and constraints upon our problems, and hence fail to solve them.

Don't feel bad if you don't solve this puzzle—most people end "up a tree" with it.

DRAW *FOUR* STRAIGHT LINES THROUGH THESE *NINE* DOTS WITHOUT RETRACING AND WITHOUT LIFTING YOUR PEN FROM THE PAPER.

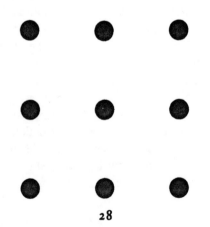

The more creative thinking you do, the more natural, rewarding, and exciting it becomes.

The creative person seldom complains of a lack of opportunity.

#28: HOSPITAL'S BONANZA

When asked to think of possible prior events or causes for a given situation, most people usually rest content with only one or two plausible explanations that occur to them. Creative people, on the other hand, prefer to generate many alternative explanations, even farfetched ones. Only after they have formulated and amassed a chockful of "hypotheses" to account for a given event, do they select the best or most likely explanation. The generation of a copious number of "hypotheses" is one of the most crucial aspects of *creative analysis.*

Get your friends to join you in this game; you'll be surprised to discover how fertile their imaginations can be when challenged to let their minds go.

A LARGE HOSPITAL ORGANIZES AN ANNUAL "FETE" IN THE COMMUNITY TO RAISE MONEY FOR THE HOSPITAL. THEY FIND THAT THIS YEAR THEIR INCOME FROM THE "FETE" FAR EXCEEDED THE PROCEEDS FROM PREVIOUS YEARS' SIMILAR VENTURES. HOW MANY PRIOR CIRCUMSTANCES CAN YOU SUGGEST TO ACCOUNT FOR THIS? LIST AS MANY IDEAS AS YOU CAN.

#29: IT'S IN THE BAG

This exercise shows that with some problems requiring a creative solution, you need to "reverse" the problem, or "stand it on its head," so to speak. How would you solve the following problem?

It was the sixteenth hole in the annual Bob Hope tournament play. The tall, handsome newcomer, who looked very much like Bing Crosby, had an excellent chance of winning. His iron shot had fallen short of the green, and he had a good chance of making a birdie. Smiling broadly and singing "Thanks for the Memories," he bounded down the fairway, then stopped short in utter dismay. His ball had rolled into a small paper bag carelessly tossed there by someone in the gallery—although it was whispered that Bob Hope had placed it there. If he removed the ball from the bag, it would cost him a penalty stroke. If he tried to hit the ball and the bag, he would lose control over the shot. For a moment, he stood there pondering over the problem. Then, to Bob's chagrin, he solved it. How did he solve it?

*Think every thought to the limit—and
then go beyond.*

*Imaginative ideas are to the mind what
your feet are to your body—without them
you cannot get anyplace.*

#30: THE SHIPWRECKED SAILOR

Most problems requiring a creative solution cannot be accomplished with traditional logical thinking in which you pro-

49

ceed in an orderly manner from point to point, supporting each step on the preceding one. The following problem does not yield itself to this kind of solution.

But you can solve it if you use your imagination to generate unusual alternatives, make deliberate jumps in your thinking, and welcome chance ideas that might occur to you. Refuse to be constrained by old ideas and boundaries and expand your horizons.

WHAT MIGHT THE HERO OF THE FOLLOWING STORY DO TO SAVE HIS LIFE? GIVE AS MANY SOLUTIONS AS YOU CAN.

A sailor, the lone survivor of a shipwreck, is washed ashore on a remote island inhabited by hostile and primitive natives who capture him. Because he is a stranger and thus threatening to them, the tribe prepares to throw him into a volcano as a sacrifice to their devil-god.

At the last moment, the tribe's sorcerer halts the sacrifice and tells the tribe that this white stranger appears to be their god whose arrival was predicted in religious writings. If he will admit to being that god, the sailor is told, he will be spared and made reigning monarch. The sailor agrees with delight.

After a week of living in splendid luxury, he learns his life is again in jeopardy because the tribe's religious writings also specify that their god can walk on water. Accordingly, a ceremony has been arranged for the next day whereby he will be paddled out many miles into the ocean where, in the presence of the entire tribe, he will perform this miracle.

A possible solution:

During his week's sojourn on the island, the sailor learned that a couple of miles off it a school of vicious killer-sharks were prowling the seas. He went to the sorcerer and proposed that for him to walk on water all the male members of the tribe (including the sorcerer) would have to take a ceremonial swim before he would step out of the boat.

The sorcerer agreed, and as the natives jumped over, they were eaten by the sharks. He returned triumphantly to the island, and as the only male member, he not only lived a life of noble ease, but also sired over 300 children.

Think of other possible solutions.

Signs depict objects, but symbols beget concepts. And concepts are the stuff our imaginations feed upon.

Originality is nothing but a fresh set of eyes and ears.

#31: NEW DIRECTIONS

It's always a challenge to communicate across a language barrier. To cope with the expected influx of foreign visitors during the Bicentennial Era, leading graphic designers have devised signs to appear in air, rail, and bus terminals nationwide for the guidance of travelers. Here are three:

BAGGAGE—CHECK-IN

TICKET PURCHASE

INFORMATION

Now it's your turn. How would you symbolize:
1. LOST AND FOUND. 2. HOTEL INFORMATION.
3. CUSTOMS INSPECTION.

Drawing skills and neatness don't count. Universality and clarity of symbols do.

> *Creative imagination transforms mere po-*
> *tentialities into hard actualities.*
>
> *Creative daydreaming is a powerful spur*
> *to achievement.*

#32: THE ROYAL WIZARD

Thinking up suitable titles for short stories is a good stretching exercise for the imagination, and fun to do in a group. It not only increases your originality and flexibility, but it obliges you to distill your understanding of the content of the story into a few evocative words.

As you work on this problem, remember that a story title in a publication often serves as a "teaser." It is used to pull the reader into the story and to convince him that his time will be well spent.

Here is a brief story that needs a better title than we've given it:

There once lived a king who depended greatly on his wise man. But, through one circumstance and another, he grew to doubt the powers and perceptions of his chosen adviser. So, to test him, he had him tossed into a rather comfortable dungeon with a huge door secured by a combination lock. The king promised that if the wise man could free himself, he would be restored to his former exalted post.

The wise man examined the combination lock and calculated that there were 288,000 possible combinations. He further calculated that, at the rate of trying one combination per minute, working an eight-hour day, he would be free in 600 days at the latest.

He made an elaborate chart to keep track of the combinations he tried, hung up his calendar, and buckled down to business as 599 days passed. Before noon of the last day, he twirled half of his quota of combinations, then partook of a light lunch.

After lunch, he took down his calendar and returned to his job whistling happily. At 4:59 P.M., he had only one more combination to go, so he placed the rolled-up calendar under his arm and smiling confidently, twisted the final combination into place.

Nothing happened! His mouth hung open in shock. He beat on the lock, but it stood firm. In frustration, he threw himself against the heavy door. Slowly, it swung open. It was then that he found that when he had first been imprisoned, the king had ordered that the cell bolt not be thrown.

WHAT TITLES CAN YOU SUGGEST
FOR THIS STORY?

When you leave the beaten path, you're apt to find something you've never seen before.

There comes a time in the life of every person when he has to abandon habit and do what is creative.

#33: OF LOVE AND LIVING

Metaphor is inextricably woven into the fabric of our language. Take, for example, seeing or visual perception. We say that we shall wait and *see*, or we want to *see* for ourselves, and not take anything *sight unseen*. We all have an *outlook* or a *viewpoint* on things, and in our reflective moments, we use our *mind's eye*. We *see* the point of a joke, and can't *see* a certain politician running for the presidency. We *see* it as our duty to *see* to it that our children are raised well, and in general, we *look* after them. It is only a short step from here to axioms that depend on metaphorical use of language as in "Love is often blind, but it seldom stays so." Or, "Love is one game that is never called because of darkness."

NOW IT'S YOUR TURN: THINK UP AN ORIGINAL METAPHOR OR SIMILE ON EACH OF THE FOLLOWING SUBJECTS: LOVE, LIFE, WORK, JOY, HOPE.

Creativity is a battle against fixed attitudes.

Frozen categories and rigid definitions cripple our minds.

#34: THE GREEK CROSS

This problem trains your ability to avoid restrictions that hamper your mind and that don't exist in the given problem statement.

TEN COINS ARE ARRANGED LIKE THIS:

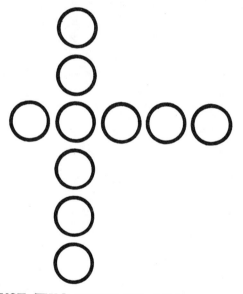

MOVE JUST *TWO* COINS TO ANOTHER POSITION SO THAT TWO ROWS, CONTAINING *SIX* COINS EACH WHEN ADDED UP EITHER HORIZONTALLY OR VERTICALLY, WILL BE FORMED. (This problem is best solved with actual coins on a table.)

The creative urge persists in spite of all opposition because it is that about human beings which is eternal.

Ambiguous ideas are frequently the most fertile ones.

#35: A MILITARY TALE

This doodle is attributed to the famous French author Victor Hugo. It illustrates how we learn to deduce the whole of an object or picture from catching a glimpse of one or more of its component parts. This is a skill that can be improved through practice, and one that has a parallel in crossword puzzles and other word games that also depend on this ability. In this case, the key lies in determining the significance of the vertical line.

*The best kind of learning is achieved only
through creating.*

*To do a job creatively, you've got to have
freedom to roam around.*

#36: SCAMS

The purpose of this exercise is to build your fluency of thought
and expression. At first, you might find that you can think of
only a few sentences; but if you persist, many more will occur to
you.

This is another great game to play with friends. See how
many sentences each of you can produce within a specified time
limit.

WRITE FIVE WORD SENTENCES FROM FIVE GIVEN
LETTERS FOR EACH WORD:

S   C   A   M   S

Examples:

Senior	citizens	arrange	maximum	security
Sarcastic	comments	are	meant	seriously

NOW IT'S YOUR TURN. SEE HOW MANY SEN-
TENCES YOU CAN PRODUCE IN EXACTLY FIVE
MINUTES.

Nature is still the wealthiest mine of in-novative discoveries.

A fresh pair of eyes and ears coupled with insatiable curiosity equal originality.

#37: NATURE'S INVENTIONS

For many modern inventions, there already exists a counterpart in nature. Here is a list of animals and of the inventions they utilize. Try matching the animal with the invention.

1. Bat	( ) Snowshoes
2. Armadillo	( ) Swaddling clothes
3. Chameleon	( ) Sonar
4. Deep-sea fishes	( ) Gun blasts and chemical attack
5. Echidna	( ) Tank
6. Squid	( ) Camouflage
7. Flying squirrel	( ) Suction cup
8. Hummingbird	( ) Anesthesia
9. Birds	( ) Electricity
10. Scorpion	( ) Helicopter
11. Snake	( ) Spurs
12. Antelope	( ) Parachute
13. Abalone	( ) Jet propulsion
14. Beetle	( ) Hypodermic
15. Caribou	( ) Signal code
16. Silkworm	( ) Plane flaps (for braking)

When you feel creative, you've already won half the battle.

When you have few ideas, you may be lucky to have a good one; when you have many ideas, you're apt to have a great one.

#38: WHAT'S FOR DINNER?

This exercise increases your ideational fluency and your ability to name things that belong in certain classes; in this case foods or drinks that are yellow.

A man came home from the office and found that his wife had just redecorated the dining room. "Tonight," she said, "we're having a dinner that matches our yellow walls," and indeed, everything she served was yellow. Name at least six foods or drinks he might have been served.

In exercising his imagination, man enriches his living experience.

Similes and metaphors are the magic wands that turn our experiences into memorable things.

#39: AS EASY AS PIE

The major secret of creativity is the ability to look at a familiar thing from different perspectives and new vantage points. It is for this reason that similes and metaphors are used deliberately in invention and creative problem-solving.

But in addition to training your inventive capacities, this exercise provides you with the opportunity to think comparatively and pictorially, to develop your own expressions which lend vitality and color to your speech and writing. And through this you will make yourself a more interesting person.

Examples: Complete the following: AS SURE AS . . .
Possible similes: birth and death; gravity; you're alive; that your shadow will follow you, etc.

AS HAPPY AS . . . a June bug; a clam at high water; a priest at a wedding; a pig in muck; a wave that dances on the sea, etc.

AS COLD AS . . . a dog's nose; the grave; cucumbers; an earthworm; an enthusiastic New England audience; Greenland's icy mountains; the ice on northern sea; the world's heart; etc.

NOW THINK UP AN ORIGINAL SIMILE TO COMPLETE:
    AS EASY AS . . .

Try to think up at least three original similes.
Now give it a twist. Instead of creating similes that mean "easy," create at least three similes that mean "difficult." This frequently lends humor to your expression. *Examples:* As easy as . . . pinning a medal on a shadow. As easy as . . . holding the wind with a net.

NOW IT'S YOUR TURN.

Just good-enough ideas are not enough—
find better ones!

The more ideas you produce, the greater
your chances of coming up with signifi-
cant ones.

#40: TARDY EMPLOYEE

This is a useful "real-life" exercise to strengthen and tone up your inventive powers. Try your best to keep your imagination moving, and produce at least five ideas to solve the problem.

IF YOU WERE THE HEAD OF A DEPARTMENT AND HAD A SUBORDINATE WHO WAS HABITUALLY LATE IN THE MORNING, BUT WHO WAS TOO VALUABLE TO FIRE, WHAT WOULD YOU DO TO CORRECT HIS TARDINESS?

Creative energy is never depleted.

Progress, in its truest sense, is possible
only when there is a surplus of creativity.

#41: PERSONALIZED PLUMBING

Bathrooms have remained essentially unchanged in design since they came indoors. In fact, a prominent university professor of architecture recently wrote a book on the subject. He pointed out that very little design attention has gone into that "much-used, but little-discussed" room. In his opinion, the washbasin is too low and poorly suited to its tasks, the bathtub is dangerous and uncomfortable, and the toilet is unsuited to the anatomy and habits of both men and women. Furthermore, bathroom storage is usually inadequate. Do you agree with these opinions?

If cost were no object, what refinements could you suggest that would make bathrooms better and commodes more commodious?

The creative person does not merely accept the unforeseeable future, he builds it into his life.

Every new creative idea is at first impossible.

#42: THE OVERLOADED DRIVER

Age and experience are not absolute requirements for problem solving. In fact, in some people, unfortunately, time serves merely to solidify prejudices and to limit flexibility. That's why sometimes a problem is more easily solved by someone who can see it with "fresh eyes" and is burdened with no preconceptions, as this story suggests.

A heavily loaded truck is approaching a tunnel. The driver suddenly realizes that his load is too high to fit into the tunnel, and he slams on his brakes at the last minute. He stops safely and steps out. Sure enough, his load is a couple of inches too high. Already, a long caravan of cars is forming behind his truck, but he can think of only two solutions to his problem: either to partially unload his truck, which would take considerable time and require his return after passing through the tunnel to retrieve objects left behind. Or, he could go forty miles out of his way, via a road with no tunnel, if he could turn around in the traffic jam he had created.

HOW WOULD YOU SOLVE THIS PROBLEM?

#43: PRIME TIME

People experienced in advertising, publishing, and broadcasting have learned that how you name a product, service, or program can make a lot of difference in how it is *received* and *perceived* by the public.

Many of the most popular television situation comedies are named either after the star, or after the character he or she plays in the series. Pick one of the programs listed below, and suggest four other titles that might have been chosen:

1. Mary Tyler Moore Show
2. Rhoda
3. The Bob Newhart Show
4. The Lucille Ball Show

#44: THE TRUCKER'S TRIAL

In a time of disaster or crisis, a person's very survival may depend on resourcefulness—which is really just another name for creative thinking. This becomes apparent if you read books and articles by individuals who unexpectedly found themselves adrift on the ocean or isolated on an Andes mountain peak. But such predicaments can occur even closer to home. For example, imagine the following situation:

A truck loaded with household goods is traveling from Chicago to the West Coast. It contains everything from the contents of kitchen cupboards to furniture to garage items. The driver tries to get through a pass in the Rockies at the height of a blizzard. The temperature is -15° and dropping. It grows dark, and there is no other traffic because now the pass has been temporarily closed. Suddenly the truck skids out of control and jackknifes, ending up disabled in a snowbank. The driver is not hurt, but is afraid he might freeze before he is found. What might he do to keep warm, or to summon help?

Common sense and the things that are taken for granted are most in need of re-examination.

Draw a circle around your specific objective; it will be easier to score a direct hit.

#45: ARABS AND ROMANS

Matches are laid out in this pattern:

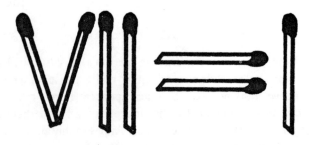

By moving only one match, make it a true equality. The solution requires that you look beyond the language in which the problem is stated. What other mathematical symbols can you devise by moving a single match? Think visually, and consider the title of this problem. Does it perhaps offer a clue?

Creativity increases a person's self-esteem and his enthusiasm for life.

The enemy of creativity is complacent self-satisfaction with the status quo.

#46: COMMON DENOMINATORS

Creative thinking frequently depends on the ability to see the similarities and differences between entities or objects. Sometimes it is a single link not immediately apparent that relates several otherwise dissimilar things. It may be an attribute like "whiteness" that links a potato and a polar bear, or a function like the ability to provide shade and shelter that links a tree and an umbrella. Inventive people have learned to make these associations very rapidly.

SELECT THE ONE WORD IN A SET OF FIVE THAT DOES NOT BELONG TO THE CLASS.

Example: Canoe, log, engine, ship, raft
Answer: Engine (all others are conveyances, or things that float.)
1. Motorcycle, carriage, car, boat, train
2. Boxing, skating, Ping-Pong, wrestling, football
3. Peanut, carrot, stringbean, potato, radish
4. Cowardly, mean, honest, rich, loyal
5. Four, fifteen, twenty, six, twenty-two
6. Indigo, ultramarine, azure, emerald, cerulean

7. Sculpture, painting, mobile, monument, bas-relief
8. Fantasy, fancy, idea, vision, reverie
9. Abasement, humiliation, criticism, disgrace, dishonor
10. Television, book, radio, magazine, game
11. Lion, hyena, giraffe, bear, wolf
12. Oak, weeping willow, maple, mahogany, pine

A problem is like a mother-in-law: you might have to live with it before you know what to do with it.

The full exercise of creative empathy would do away with much misunderstanding and strife.

#47: IT'S ALL RELATIVE

Human relations, particularly marital ones, are always important concerns in both life and literature. From Shakespeare to the modern soap opera, from movies to the neighborhood cocktail party, you can hardly escape hearing wry observations about husbands, wives, and their attendant in-laws. In fact, it's hard to find anyone without an opinion on these matters—even among the unmarried.

Surely it's time you took a shot or two at our most popular—yet problem-laden—institutions. Think up three epigrams involving relatives (blood or acquired).
Example: "To be the son of a poor man is fate; to be his son-in-law is sheer stupidity."

Most people surround themselves with arbitrary and artificial limitations, and then blame life for them.

Awareness, sensitivity, wonder, and curiosity are the four wheels that set the creativity engine into motion.

#48: CONCERNED UNCLE

The two most common habits or attitudes that block us from solving problems effectively are (1) Our natural tendency to latch on to the first notion that occurs to us, and then bolt with it —frequently into a precipice, or at least into a more serious problem than the original one we started out with; and (2) Our tendency *not* to allow our creative deliberation to have free reign without restraint from our critical faculties. So ingrained is this habit of simultaneously weighing and judging ideas while in the process of producing them that it takes deliberate, sustained training to separate these two functions.

This exercise asks you first not to rest content with the first suggestion that occurs to you, even if you feel that it represents the best solution to the problem; and second, to produce as many feasible, or even offbeat solutions, you can think of. There is always plenty of time later to screen your ideas and weed out the untenable.

YOU HAVE DISCOVERED YOUR FAVORITE FOUR-TEEN-YEAR-OLD NEPHEW HAS STARTED TO DRINK ALCOHOLIC BEVERAGES. WHAT IDEAS COULD YOU THINK UP TO INDUCE HIM TO STOP?

Nothing is as valuable as a good idea, but nothing is so powerfully a sure thing as a good idea whose time has come.

Strive for what is great; little things will take care of themselves.

#49: CONSCIENCE MONEY

Reasoning backward from consequences to causes is especially good mental exercise. All you have to guide you is a stated or observed event or phenomenon, and your fertile imagination. Used as an adult game, this sort of problem can produce some very amusing and fanciful results.

Remember, there is no one "right" answer. All—or none—of the explanations you and your friends devise may be "true." Despite our human tendency to simplify, the world seldom co-operates; events are usually multidetermined.

Now try your hand at explaining this:

THE MANAGEMENT OF A DEPARTMENT STORE WITH A HIGH PILFERAGE RATE IS PLEASANTLY SURPRISED TO FIND THAT, THIS MONTH, A SUB-STANTIAL AMOUNT OF STOLEN MERCHANDISE HAS BEEN RETURNED BY MAIL.

HOW MANY EXPLANATIONS OR PRIOR CIRCUM-STANCES CAN YOU SUGGEST TO ACCOUNT FOR THIS?

A first-rate pizza pie is more creative than a second-rate musical composition.

The creative person cares little for what has been, he is preoccupied with what might and will be.

#50: MAKE SOMETHING OF IT—II

The ability to make various visual associations and connections between apparently unrelated elements is as important to creativity as the ability to relate verbal elements.

On the following pages, you will find two sets of lines or drawing fragments. Study them until your visual imagination suggests a total picture using all the elements. Find as many ways to tie these fragments together as you can.

Remember that there is no "solution," no "hidden drawing" —any more than in the clouds you saw shapes in as a child.

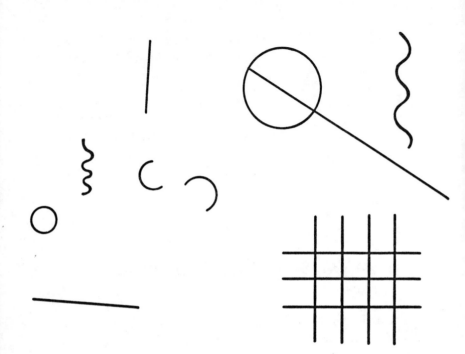

INTERMEDIATE TEST B: TIRES

IN EXACTLY FIVE (5) MINUTES, LIST ALL POSSIBLE
USES FOR TIRES (MOTORCYCLE, BICYCLE, ETC.).

Metaphor and simile are the starting points of creative thinking.

Whenever thinking is powered by excitement, enthusiasm, and energy, creativity is displayed.

#51: STRIKING SIMILARITIES

Simile and metaphor are one of the most ancient forms of speech. They have proven themselves essential to every form of human utterance. The Old Testament abounds in similes and metaphors that are now current coin: "Still as a stone," "White as snow," "Boil like a pot," "Unstable as water," "Sharp as a two-edged sword," "Melted like wax," etc.

Similes and metaphors are not mere figures of speech, frills, or devices to vivify language. They are inextricably bound up with language and thought. They give us unique insights into reality, new ways of looking at things, new contexts for viewing the old and familiar.

COMPLETE THE FOLLOWING SIMILES.

Example: "Money is like promises,
Possible ending: easier made than kept."—Josh Billings
  1. "Wishes, like castles in the air,
  2. "Time is like money;
  3. "The world is like a great staircase;
  4. "Ambition is like love;
  5. "Money is like manure;
  6. "A woman, like a melon,
  7. "Advice is like kissing:
  8. "Truth shines like the sun;
  9. "Prejudice, like the spider,
  10. "Love, like a cough,

Don't get discouraged—you can always start all over again.

The secret of mental youth is creativity.

#52: WORD CHAINS

Most creative people are noted for the voluminous vocabulary they have at their command. The more words you can think of, the more readily you can form associations. Words represent ideas, and most creative new ideas are the result of a thinking process called association of ideas. By exercising your vocabulary, you increase your power to identify, associate, and relate ideas, thus toning up your creative mind. Compete with friends.

Here are a series of four-letter words that have nothing in common. By changing only one letter at a time, think of a series of words to build a bridge between the two.

Example: Work/lame
1. Work, pork, pore, tore, tome, tame, lame
2. Work, cork, core, come, came, lame
3. Work, wore, lore, lare, lame

The fewer words you use to build the bridge, the better.

NOW EXPERIMENT WITH THESE:

1. FIRE/MINT
2. LOVE/PART
3. RISE/BATH
4. CAME/DIRT
5. HATE/LOVE
6. FIND/LOSE
7. NEST/MEAN
8. SWIM/CLIP
9. GIVE/TAKE
10. TOUR/SORT
11. MALE/WORD
12. MISS/BASE
13. CAKE/BILL
14. MEAN/SOAP
15. PAVE/TORT
16. WILD/MORE
17. BOOK/LIST

*Many a creative idea becomes just a flash
in the pan because of lack of persistence.*

*Fear of failure is the most devastating
block to creativity.*

#53: FIGURE COMPLETION

This exercise will increase your capacity for observation and spatial judgment (seeing the system of relations between figures)—all extremely vital for certain kinds of creative problem-solving.

EXAMINE THE FOLLOWING SETS OF FIGURES HORIZONTALLY, VERTICALLY AND DIAGONALLY, AND FIGURE OUT THE PATTERN. DRAW A FIGURE IN THE VACANT SPACE THAT YOU THINK COMPLETES EACH SERIES.

I.

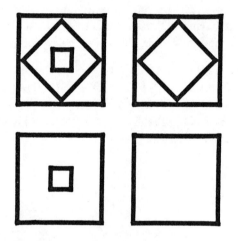

2.

74

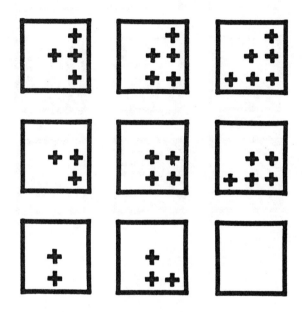

3.

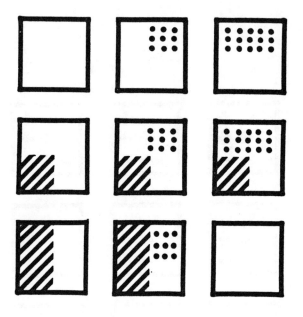

4.

We fail only because we give up too soon.

Man is a problem-solving creature.

#54: WORDS . . . WORDS . . . WORDS

This exercise enhances your ability to discern or recognize words in the "scrambled" letters of a given word.

It is also another good test of persistence. Most people find that they could have doubled the number of words they found, had they stuck with the task a little longer.

FROM THE FOLLOWING WORD MAKE AS MANY WORDS OF AT LEAST FOUR LETTERS EACH AS YOU CAN:

C O M P R E H E N S I V E

It is also possible to turn a silk purse into a sow's ear if you squander the creative potential that is within you.

Practice and persistence are the necessary ingredients of creativity.

#55: WHAT'S THE DRIFT?

Effective problem-solvers are noted for their keen observational powers. Alertness of observation frequently provides the necessary clues which lead to effective solutions to problems.

This exercise is designed to train and strengthen your observational ability.

IN THE FOLLOWING SERIES, THE WORDS ARE RELATED NOT BY MEANING, BUT BY SPELLING. FIND THE RELATIONSHIP AND THE RULE USED IN CREATING EACH SERIES.

Example:

UNIFORM DUNGEON STUNNING IMMUNITY
TRIBUNAL THEREUNDER EXCOMMUNICATE
SUPERABUNDANCE

Answer: The letters "un" move with each word one letter to the
right.
Now try these series:

1. FRIENDLIEST SIESTA DISINTERESTED SUPERCELESTIAL
   INCONTESTABLE FESTERING PRESTIGIOUS
   SUGGESTIVENESS PESTILENTIAL DESTRUCTIVELY
   ESTABLISHMENT

2. ARTFUL SPECTACULAR TARTLY SWEETHEART STARVE
   SURCHARGE RETARDED SMARTLY FOREARM SMARTING

3. BATH THINK PITHY ETHEREAL LEATHER METHADONE
   STEALTHILY DEATHLESS FEATHERY

4. ANTAGONISM COMMANDANT CANTALOUPE DILETTANTE
   PLANTATION SUPPLANTED SYNANTHOUS IMPLANTING
   PHANTASM ROMANTIC BANTER SHANTY ANTE CANT

5. ROTUNDA ORATION PRONOUNCE NORTHERN
   CHROMATIC FLORESCENCE METROPOLIS UNCORRECTED
   PRIMROSE SARTORIAL RAPTUROUS IMMEMORIAL
   METACHROMATIC METAPHOR

*In creativity you deal with shades of gray,
not with blacks and whites.*

*If you want to be creative, you have to
have the courage to think in uncharted
waters, without floundering.*

#56: MAY DAY

The ability and willingness to persist in the search for the full
and accurate explanation of an observed fact is an almost indis-
pensable creative attribute. Scientists, among others, depend on
this ability to generate alternative hypotheses. Always remember
that one explanation doesn't necessarily rule out another. Many
circumstances and events are multiply-determined.

HERE, THEN, IS A STATEMENT WHICH MAY OR
MAY NOT BE TRUE, BUT WHICH YOU ARE TO *AS-
SUME* IS TRUE OR VALID. GIVE AS MANY PLAUSI-
BLE OR REASONABLE EXPLANATIONS AS YOU
CAN:

MAY IS THE MONTH OF THE LARGEST NUMBER
OF SUICIDES.

*Most failures are due to our tendency to
give up too soon.*

*Every new beginning provides us with the
opportunity to use our minds creatively.*

#57: WORDS APLENTY

When done as a solo problem, this exercise helps you develop
persistence in problem-solving. As a competitive game, this exercise takes on additional aspects. The time limit exercises participants' ability to make decisions under pressure and to anticipate
the long-range consequences of those decisions.

Words Aplenty is more than a way to pass the time. It sharpens your mental acuity and increases your available vocabulary —those words you can use in expressing yourself, as distinguished from the much larger number of words you merely read and recognize.

EPAESNTAEONREOLTEANNPSOTE

Put the twenty-five letters above into the twenty-five squares below so as to form two-, three-, four-, or five-letter words both horizontally and vertically. Use each letter only once and use all the letters. Abbreviations, foreign and proper names are not allowed. Words requiring hyphens or apostrophes are also forbidden.

The object is to form the maximum number of words. Scoring: Each letter that is part of a word counts 5 points.

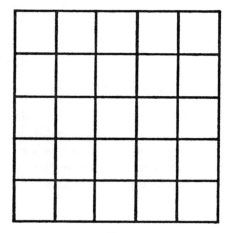

Examples from the letters given:

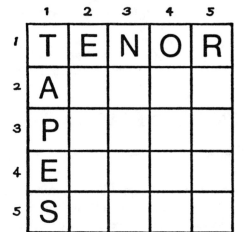

1 across:
TENOR: 25; TEN: 15;
NOR: 15; NO: 10;
OR: 10 = 75 points

1 down:
TAPES: 25; APES: 20;
TAP: 15 = 60 points

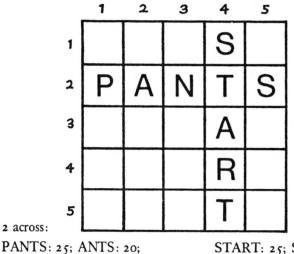

2 across:
PANTS: 25; ANTS: 20;
PAN: 15; AN: 10 = 70
points

4 down:
START: 25; STAR: 20;
TART: 20; ART: 15;
TAR: 15 = 95 points

The best workshop for creativity is held within the one-man classroom of your head.

Failure to use your natural creativity is not only waste, it is self-betrayal.

#58: RHYME AND REASON

Exercises in rhyming release creative energy; they stir imagination and fancy into action.

While doing this exercise, remember that rhyme is frequently a matter of sound, or what is technically known as phonetics, and does not always have to involve similar or identical spelling.

Poetry, utilizing rhyme, preceded prose, and continues to this day to be a favorite literary expression. Rhyme can be used either to arouse lofty emotions, or the lighter and more frivolous ones. This exercise deals with the latter.

After each "definition" write two *rhyming words* to which it refers.

Examples:

1. Large hog   — big pig
2. Television   — boob tube
3. Cooperative female   — game dame

Now try these:

1. Happy father   —
2. False pain   —
3. Formed like a simian   —
4. Highest-ranking policeman   —
5. Voyage by a large boat   —
6. Corpulent feline   —
7. Melancholy fellow   —
8. Clever beginning   —

9. Heavy and unbroken slumber —
10. Crazy custom —
11. Lengthy melody —
12. Weak man —
13. Instruction at the seashore —
14. Criticism lacking in effectiveness —
15. A person who murders for pleasurable excitement —
16. Musical string instrument with full, rich and soft sounds —
17. Courageous person who is owned as property by another —
18. Mature complaint —
19. Strange hair growing on the lower part of a man's face —
20. Drooping marine crustacean —
21. A man, short in height, accompanying a woman —

Few things are as gratifying as creative fulfillment.

A person who wants to create rather than possess attains a higher level of psychological health and peace of mind.

#59: DISTANT RELATIONS

This exercise resembles #1—*Kindred Relations*—except that the individual items are somewhat more difficult and you have to also think of at least two additional words or expressions that go with the key word.

THINK OF A FIFTH WORD THAT IS RELATED TO THE PRECEDING FOUR WORDS. (YOU CAN FORM COMPOUND, HYPHENATED WORDS IN SOME CASES, OR COMMONLY USED EXPRESSIONS). AFTER YOU HAVE FOUND THE FIFTH WORD, THINK OF AT LEAST TWO ADDITIONAL WORDS THAT CAN BE USED WITH IT.

Example:

Dream   plan   legion   all   _____

Answer: American (American dream, American plan, American legion, all-American).

Examples of other words that can be used with "American": American cheese, American eagle, American English, American Indian, etc.

NOW PRACTICE YOUR ASSOCIATIVE SKILLS WITH THE FOLLOWING SETS:

1.	HOUSE	TOP	FACE	CATCHER	_____
2.	DOWN	WHISTLE	CALL	CRY	_____
3.	POT	APPEAL	OPPOSITE	HYGIENE	_____
4.	RICH	OUT	DUMB	DOWN	_____
5.	BOX	SHEET	CHAMBER	STAND	_____
6.	LOVE	LEAVE	CALL	BAY	_____
7.	VALUE	JACKET	END	LEARNING	_____
8.	OFFICE	CAMERA	CARDBOARD	SPRING	_____
9.	PIPE	LAND	LAY	BASKET	_____
10.	CHICKEN	TIME	CLEANING	LOCK	_____
11.	PAINTING	PRINT	BOWL	NAIL	_____
12.	CHINA	WHITE	MEAL	ASH	_____
13.	SCREEN	SALE	WATER	STORM	_____
14.	OPERA	VERSE	RED	HOUSE	_____
15.	HUMOR	NATURE	FAME	TAKE	_____
16.	EDITOR	FATHER	FOLK	HALL	_____
17.	TAP	GAUZE	SERVICE	HIGH	_____
18.	UNDER	BROKE	GO	AFTER	_____
19.	FORTH	GUARD	POLITIC	ENGLISH	_____
20.	UNCLE	OVEN	TREAT	COURAGE	_____

Hidden likenesses furnish the key to creative solutions.

We live in a complicated age and look for complicated solutions—when frequently the simple would work better.

#60: IN AND OUT LETTERS

Creative solutions to problems are often simple, elegant, even obvious. Yet, it is the "obvious" that frequently escapes our notice because we have been conditioned to look for the complicated when solving problems.

DETERMINE THE SYSTEM BEING USED TO PLACE EITHER INSIDE OR OUTSIDE THE CIRCLE ALL THE LETTERS OF THE ALPHABET. A GOES INSIDE, B BELONGS OUTSIDE, C BELONGS OUTSIDE, D BELONGS OUTSIDE, E GOES IN THE CIRCLE. WHERE DO F, G, AND THE REST OF THE ALPHABET BELONG? WHAT IS THE SYSTEM BEING USED?

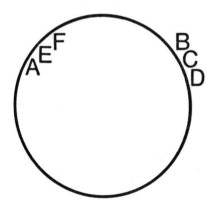

Bad times provide the acid test to man's creative capacities.

A society which restricts the freedom of creative revision is doomed to atrophy and decay.

#61: A STICKY PROBLEM

Suppose your community, for whatever reasons, discontinued garbage collection permanently. (This idea is hardly farfetched in these days of bankrupt cities.) Might you and your neighbors use this occasion to reexamine some basic assumptions? Is there some garbage that needn't be collected at all? Is it really true that municipal governments can do the job best? Would individual contractors do it cheaper? What industry could use it for recycling into new products? In short, is there a better way?

WHAT MIGHT YOU AND YOUR NEIGHBORS DO TO INVESTIGATE AND RESOLVE THE PROBLEM? FIND AT LEAST SIX POSSIBILITIES.

Most people look at what is; they never see what can be.

Approach challenges with gusto; let others rest on the dubious laurels of self-satisfaction.

#62: HIDDEN ORCHESTRA

This game gives you yet another opportunity to liberate yourself from the restrictions of conformity and habit. Most children find this exercise easy to do, while many adults experience difficulties, at least with some of the given sentences. See if you can do better than you did with *Concealed Colors*.

THE NAME OF WHAT MUSICAL INSTRUMENT IS CONCEALED IN EACH SENTENCE?

1. Cast a net in these waters for they are teeming with fish.
2. Clean the tub after you've taken a bath.
3. An old hobo established himself at the rich man's doorstep.
4. He intends to spin Ethel real good on the dance floor.
5. Look at this rich man doling out his money so sparingly.
6. The cell of the prisoner was raided for hidden narcotics.
7. The government fails to ban journalistic excesses.
8. It is no longer permissible to bug legislative proceedings.
9. The Greek government did not accord the Ionian Islands independence.
10. I wouldn't trust her; she'll blab as soon as she's left the house.
11. After you've figured out pi, a norm is established for the rest of the geometrical problems.
12. Your deep-seated rancor nets you nothing.
13. Clean the wound thoroughly or gangrene will set in.
14. Lonely reindeers walked across the fields.
15. The dinner was blah, or not exactly to his liking.
16. The car market experiences a glut every spring.

If you have no problems, create some.

To reach virtuosity in creative thinking, it has to be practiced continuously.

#63: THE COMPULSIVE SMOKER

We are frequently too hasty and impatient in solving problems, and as a result, we overlook the "obvious." This problem illustrates how easy it is to overlook a simple element which sometimes is the key to a correct solution.

A heavy smoker wakes up in the middle of the night at 2 A.M. and finds himself out of cigarettes. He gets dressed and rushes out, but the streets are deserted and all the stores, restaurants and bars are closed. Arriving back in his apartment he looks through all the wastepaper baskets and ashtrays for butts, figuring out that with five butts he can make a new cigarette. He finds twenty-five butts—enough to last him until the stores open, if he smokes one cigarette every hour.

HOW LONG DID HIS SUPPLY LAST?

We don't observe things with which we are most familiar.

When you work up your imagination to the state of vision, you've already done it.

#64: DRAW YOUR WATCH

Creativity requires exact, recallable observation. It requires that we make discriminating and refined use of our senses.

ON A PIECE OF PAPER, DRAW THE FACE OF YOUR
WATCH WITHOUT LOOKING AT IT.

Now look at the result. Chances are that you missed a few
important details, or drew them wrong—almost everybody does.

Creative solutions should be looked for,
not forced.

Imagination was made to be enjoyed.

#65: SPELL IT OUT

Although this problem is presented in numerical terms, consider
the possibility that the solution may *not* lie in the mathematical
manipulation of the symbols. We are often misled by the apparent familiarity of the problem "type" into assuming the nature
of the answer. With that caution in mind, find the general rule
that governs the series:

18, 11, 15, 14, 19, 16, 13, 12, 20

True understanding comes only through creativity.

What the creative process has to offer is what most people need today—intellectually, socially, and for their psychological health.

#66: WHAT WOULD HAPPEN IF—II

The "what if" attitude—essential for liberating imagination—is dismissed by many adults as a childish make-believe, and is, as a consequence, underemphasized in our educational programs.

This exercise gives you a chance to dig deeper into the game of imaginative thinking. It will enable you to break out of habitual thinking patterns that hamper the emergence of new ideas.

You can make the game more entertaining and stimulating by involving several of your friends.

List as many possible consequences of the following unusual happening as you can.

WHAT WOULD HAPPEN IF YOU DIDN'T HAVE TO SLEEP?

The creative person transforms problems into challenges for his fertile mind.

Most people habitually hide themselves even from their own new ideas, and thus miss or mismanage many opportunities.

#67: OCCUPATIONS

This exercise will increase your verbal and conceptual fluency within a specified framework.

WRITE THE NAMES OF AS MANY OCCUPATIONS AS YOU CAN THAT BEGIN WITH THE LETTER S AND END WITH THE LETTER R. (These occupations can be formed also with hyphenated or compound words).

Examples: Social worker, Sky-diver, etc.

An idea that appears radical, bizarre, or way-out one day, may be readily accepted the next day.

A good creative idea always collides with an old idea, and some individuals find this very frightening.

#68: COMMUNITY SERVICE

One of the least recognized aspects of creativity is one that has immense practical application—the ability to organize and interrelate the experience, skills and talents of others, to form a new entity.

Just as the artist uses shapes and colors to create new and pleasing configurations, so the creative organizer combines the strengths of many qualified and motivated people, building a smoothly functioning organization.

Let's suppose that, as one of the town's leading citizens, you have been asked by the mayor to organize a volunteer ambulance corps. You know nothing much about medicine, ambulances, community needs, or existing facilities. How would you proceed?

Apparently insoluble problems, after they are solved, seem simple and even obvious.

When you become conscious of your fixed ideas, you've found a way to more creative and nourishing alternatives of acting.

#69: UPENDED BOTTLE

This classic parlor puzzle illustrates the difficulty most of us have in freeing ourselves from set notions when dealing with problems. Most people will attempt to yank the five-dollar bill from beneath the bottle, which won't solve the problem.

There are two ingenious solutions for this problem. Try to work out the solutions in your mind, before making any trial-and-error attempts.

PLACE A FIVE-DOLLAR BILL FLAT ON A TABLE. TURN AN EMPTY COKE (OR ANY OTHER) BOTTLE UPSIDE-DOWN SO THAT ITS MOUTH RESTS ON THE CENTER OF THE BILL. WITHOUT TIPPING OVER THE BOTTLE—AND ALLOWING *NOTHING* TO TOUCH THE BOTTLE OTHER THAN THE *BILL* OR THE *TABLE*—REMOVE THE FIVE-DOLLAR BILL FROM BENEATH THE BOTTLE.

Exercising imagination opens the door to your capacities. It is then up to you to use them productively.

In creative problem-solving you need all the help you can get—from yourself.

#70: INSTANT IMAGINATION

This exercise resembles #3—*Tell a Story*—but is more demanding in that you have to decide in advance what type of story you will tell or write: lead newspaper story, dialogue, or a detective story.

When playing it with others, score a very good and original story 5 points, and a poor one 1 point.

VIVIDLY IMAGINE THE GIVEN OBJECT AND SITUATION IN FRONT OF YOU. THEN WRITE OR TELL A STORY ABOUT WHAT YOU SEE IN YOUR MIND'S EYE, USING AS GUIDES THESE THREE QUESTIONS:

1. WHAT PRECEDED OR LED UP TO THIS?
2. WHAT IS GOING ON NOW?
3. WHAT COULD THE OUTCOME BE?

BE SURE TO USE *ALL* THESE THREE QUESTIONS.

STIMULUS OBJECT AND SITUATION: UNFINISHED LETTER AND ROOM IN DISARRAY.

Without creativity, life will pass you by; with creativity, you will live life to the hilt.

The only blind date that doesn't disappoint is the one you can make with your own creative self.

#71: MANY THINGS

One of the most potent creative techniques is the finding—or seeing—or deliberately seeking—of connections or relationships between seemingly unrelated things. Many inventions have come from individuals who make it a habit to look for and find new, hitherto undiscovered, relationships between existing things.

The following exercise is presented in a form of a fable. The things between which you have to find a common relationship or principle are italicized.

A king returned from foreign wars to his castle. Bone-weary, he fell into a deep sleep and soon had a vivid dream. In his dream he saw a number of things in rapid succession. He saw first the simple shape of a *bed*. Shortly it disappeared and in its place he saw the *earth* and stones and a patch of green lawn. This too disappeared and he saw the opening of a *grave*.

A little later he saw a mighty *tree* with lush foliage and many *branches*, a big *sword* in its *sheath*, a *cell* in a *monastery*, a glowing *fireside*, a *snow-tipped summit*, and a *calm sea*, which was as flat as a mirror. Then he saw something which seemed to be a *heart*, and subsequently he beheld an *oasis* in the desert, a *camel*, a *ship*, and finally the *bed* which he had seen before.

The king was haunted by this dream for days, although he couldn't make out what it signified. Finally he decided to seek counsel from his wise man.

After he had recounted his dream, the wise man asked him: "You have seen a great many things. What meaning do you see in them?"

The king answered: "The bed signifies sleep and pleasant or fearful dreams. The earth and the stones and the lawn make me think of the seed which is placed in the soil, and of planting and harvesting. The grave signifies death.

"The mighty tree has many meanings for me: the nourishment of its fruit, the use to which I can put the timber, and the cooling shadow it grants on a hot summer day. The sword reminds me of war, the monastic cell of the peace of God, the fireside makes me think of the happy times I had with the queen before she passed away, and the snow-tipped summit recalls the daring and perseverance which is required to climb it. The ocean suggests long journeys and unknown countries. The heart is the center and the source of my life. The oasis in the desert means sweet refreshment. The camel and the ship are means of transportation, and finally I return to the restfulness of the bed."

"That is right," said the wise man, "but I could just as well say it is not so. For above the many things which you have seen and the many meanings which they suggest to you, there is one single purpose which they all serve and which you have failed to mention."

WHAT SINGLE PURPOSE DID THE WISE MAN SEE IN THE MANY THINGS THE KING HAD DREAMT OF?

Imagination knows no boundaries.

The lifeblood of success is a constant stream of new ideas.

#72: IDEATION

Directly, by doing the games and exercises, and indirectly, by reflection and the effort you've put in to accomplish these tasks, you've learned a great deal about creativity. Now it is time to put your knowledge to a test.

CREATE EIGHT SENTENCES, FOR WHICH THE EIGHT-LETTER WORD I D E A T I O N WOULD BE THE ACRONYM. ALL STATEMENTS SHOULD RE-FLECT IN SOME WAY YOUR THOUGHTS ABOUT THE SUBJECT OF CREATIVITY.

Example:

Ideas are powered by excitement and curiosity.

Daring ideas are like trump cards in your hands.

Express your strongest idea today; tomorrow may be too late.

Amass knowledge; it is the only thing you can give away and still retain.

The creative urge is just as strong as the procreative urge, and sometimes it is more fun, if only because it lasts longer.

If you find no solution to your problem, redefine it.

Opportunity is constantly pounding on the doors of those who think creatively.

Nay-sayers to new ideas may hurt others, but they hurt themselves most.

NOW IT'S YOUR TURN.

Creativity doesn't rely on magic, it is simply a way of life.

Man's imagination and the bottom of the sea are unfathomable.

#73: BECOME AN APPLE

For the solution of many types of problems, we need to use all our senses: sight, smell, sound, taste, and touch. When our senses are keen and developed, they have a wonderful way of augmenting each other. They especially enhance our visual imagery, which can be used to find innovative and often overlooked solutions to our problems.

This exercise is designed to increase the *clarity* and *control* of combined sensory imagery, and it is best done in a group.

1. Ask one of the participants to be the narrator.
2. Give each of the participants an apple.
3. Have everybody relax in a comfortable position.
4. Have the narrator read the following. He should read slowly, seriously, and soothingly, giving everyone present plenty of time to fully establish the images before he goes on to the next image. It helps to have agreed upon a prearranged signal—a lifted finger, for example—when everyone has the image fully developed, at which point the narrator can go on to the next statement.

"First close your eyes and relax. Direct your attention inward. Now imagine yourself in a familiar setting in which you would enjoy eating an apple. Relaxedly attend the sensory mood and detail of this place. Now, imagine that in your hand you have a delicious, crisp apple. Feel the apple's coolness, its weight, its firmness, its round volume, its waxy smoothness. Explore its stem. Visually examine details, see bruises, the way sunlight sparkles on the facets of the apple's form, the way the skin reflects a pattern of streaks and dots, many colors, not just one. Attend to this image till your mouth waters. Now bite the apple. Hear its juicy snap, savor its texture, its flavor. Smell the apple's sweet fragrance. With a knife, slice the apple to see what's inside. As you continue to explore the apple in detail, return occasionally to the larger context, see your hand, feel the soft breeze, be aware of the three-dimensionality of form and space.

"How was your apple this time? Probably a lot better. But your apple is probably still not as vivid as possible, simply because you don't really know what an apple is like. We've all eaten plenty of apples, but how often do we really pay attention. We are most often doing something else while eating, talking, reading, thinking, but never attending to every sensory detail. We're going to give each of you an apple now (hand out the apples) and you can eat it. We're going to ask that no one talk.

97

All of your attention should be on the apple and on your sensations. Before you eat your apple, take a minute to examine it. Look at its shape, its volume, its color, its markings. Feel its temperature, its texture, its firmness, its mass. When you really know it, take a bite from it. Listen, smell, taste, feel, attend every sensory detail. Take your time.

"The apple that you have just eaten is now being assimilated by your digestive system. The apple is becoming you. Imagine that you are the apple that you have just eaten. Imagine that you are an apple on an apple tree. Take a deep breath. Let it out, and as you let it out, relax all tensions. Quiet all distracting thinking. Direct all of your attention, in a very relaxed way, to the pleasurable thought of being an apple on a real apple tree in a beautiful apple orchard way out in the country. You can feel the warm sun on your skin. You can feel a soft breeze. The sky is clear blue. The sun feels good as it radiates into your apple body. You can hear the leaves of your tree rustling in the breeze. You can smell the fragrance of the ripening apple orchard. It feels good to be part of nature. Now imagine that you are regressing in time. You are an apple that is going backward in time, becoming smaller, smaller, greener, tarter, smaller yet, you are evolving in reverse into an apple blossom. You are an apple blossom together with many other apple blossoms on your apple tree. You can smell the lush fragrance of apple blossoms. You can feel the warm sun on your delicate petals. You can hear the honey bees buzzing as they go about pollinating the orchard. In the distance you can hear a farmer's dog barking. You can taste your own sweet nectar. You can feel that you are an integral part of an incredibly complex natural process involving sun, earth, air, bees, the seasons. It feels good.

"Now you are becoming aware that you are more than a single apple blossom. You are an apple tree. Allow your imagination to move into the branch that supports the blossom. You can feel the sap that brings energy to the tree's leaves and blossoms. You can feel the sap moving through you. Follow this flow of energy down into the trunk of the apple tree. Feel the strength of the trunk in your own body. You must be strong to support branches loaded with ripe apples, and to resist the force of heavy wind. Feel the rough texture of your bark, the hardness of your wood.

"Now direct your attention down the trunk and into the roots of your apple tree. Reach out into the dark, damp soil. See the darkness. Smell the fragrance of the fertile soil. See the fat worms and the other subterranean creatures that work the earth. Feel the cool wetness and texture of the moist dirt and rocks, as your roots reach out for life-giving water and nutrients.

"Now leave the tree. Become the water itself in the damp orchard field. Feel yourself feeding the grasses and the wildflowers. You are part of a larger concept. You are essential to life. You are part of the much larger unity of nature. As water saturated in the orchard field, experience the sun's heat drawing you upward. Feel the sun evaporating your body, transforming your liquid nature into vaporous water. Feel your molecules rising upward into the blue sky toward the blazing sun. You and the others are now forming into a soft cloud. Down below you can see the earth, the tiny patch of the apple orchard, you are floating in the blue sky effortlessly. Quiet, billowy, incredibly free. In the distance a hawk is soaring. You are part of the creative cycles of nature.

"Now the sky is darkening, becoming cooler, you can feel the wind swirling and moving through your cloud. You are condensing with other molecules into droplets of rain. Falling downward, through the cold gray sky, downward, downward. You splash the leaves of a green apple tree and fall down to the ground, to the soil, to the roots, to the strong trunk, to the sap that feeds the branches, the leaves, the blossoms, the apple. You are the apple on the tree, in the orchard, on a rainy day. You can hear the rain splattering on the leaves, feel the cold stormy wind swaying the tree branches, smell the rich odor of damp earth. Your apple, created by this marvelous interwoven working of nature, is inside you, becoming you. And you, in turn, are a unique part of this creative unity. As you return now to your aliveness, here, and now, you feel good to be part of a unity which is inherently and eternally creative."

The "I wonder if" and the "I doubt whether" attitudes make uncomfortable bedfellows. Only the "wonder if" attitude can lead to creative achievement.

Nothing can really guarantee happiness, but creativity holds the greatest promise.

#74: OBJECTION OVERRULED

As important as the ability to generate new ideas is the skill to convince others of their worth. This is true in both business and personal life. Here, then, is an exercise that will tax both your inventive powers and your sales ability. This makes an amusing and constructive party game and can be done in teams.

Choose one of the following problems in persuasion, and try to anticipate and have an adequate answer for any possible objection your audience may have.

1. Persuade your mate (or someone playing the role) that this year you should take separate vacations.
2. Convince your boss (or his stand-in) that you should be permitted—indeed encouraged—to spend two days a week working at home.

*The road to solving big problems is paved
with small solutions.*

*You can master the future of your here-
and-now if you use your imagination.*

#75: SOLVE YOUR PERSONAL PROBLEMS

Most of us have personal problems of various kinds. About some of these we can do little or nothing, and we should practice serenity to accept them. But most of our problems are amenable to creative solutions.

LIST THE PROBLEMS YOU FEEL ARE MOST IN NEED OF CREATIVE SOLUTIONS AND APPLY THE TECHNIQUES AND PRINCIPLES YOU LEARNED IN THIS BOOK TO SOLVE THEM.

In order to help you arrive at the most pressing problems you may have, consider the following:

1. What would I really like to do, have, or accomplish?
2. What more would I like to get out of my life?
3. In what areas would I like to improve my skills and abilities?
4. What bothered, annoyed, or angered me recently?
5. What do I complain most about?
6. What worries me most?
7. What makes me uncomfortable, anxious, tense?
8. What frustrates me most?
9. What recent misunderstandings have I had?
10. Whose attitudes toward myself would I like to improve?
11. What would I have to change in myself?
12. What takes too long to do?
13. What is too complicated?
14. What tires me out easily?
15. How could I organize my time better?

Now write out the problem or problems you would like to

tackle first. Do it in a narrative form and then reduce it down to as simple and clear question or statement as you can. Writing down your problems enables you to crystallize your thoughts. The act of writing them down also commits you to do something about them and provides the needed motivational push.

POST-TEST: PINS AND NEEDLES

IN EXACTLY FIVE (5) MINUTES, LIST ALL POSSIBLE USES FOR PINS AND NEEDLES.

Part II: Examples and Answers

PRE-TEST: WOODEN BLOCKS

Examples: 1. As a paperweight. 2. As a weapon to throw at an intruder. 3. As bookends. 4. As firewood. 5. As props under wood-plank sidewalks. 6. Build a raft. 7. To anchor magazines and newspapers on a newsstand. 8. To break windows. 9. As a doorstop. 10. Use as a hammer. 11. As a step or steps. 12. As an ashtray when hollowed. 13. Build a room divider. 14. As a candle holder. 15. As a toy. 16. To draw rectangles and squares. 17. Make wooden shoes. 18. Make sawdust to sprinkle on icy walks. 19. As lawn markers. 20. As a lamp base. 21. A footrest. 22. A base for clay model. 23. Carve to make objects of art (sculpture). 24. Use as a wedge to keep car from rolling when on an incline. 25. For building doghouse. 26. For weight lifting (infants). 27. To develop good posture when balanced on head. 28. As a primitive form of inducing anesthesia. 29. As mud scraper. 30. Support for shelves. 31. Pulverize for surface decor with glue. 32. As a visual aid for drawing perspective. 33. As a cigarette support. 34. A bug hider. 35. Counterbalance weight. 36. A throwing device. 37. To mark spot on treasure hunt. 38. Sell for living. 39. As a target. 40. Make picture frame. 41. Make a wall. 42. Carve on. 43. Build tower to jump off. 44. Build tree house. 45. To step on when there's mud. 46. For dogs to play with. 47. Build a fence. Etc. etc.

These are only a few examples of the uses for wooden blocks. You probably listed many others not given here.

Flexibility, fluency, and originality are three of the most vital attributes for solving problems creatively and for coping with change. This and the other three tests in this book are aimed at measuring your progress on these three all-important qualities.

In creative problem-solving it is necessary that we let our minds wander without fixating or categorizing our thoughts prematurely. If we can do this, we can prevent, what has been aptly termed as the "hardening of the categories."

This "hardening of the categories" is frequently the result of overfamiliarity with certain objects. As the late professor John E. Arnold of Stanford University put it: "We see a pencil as only a writing instrument; we never see it as a tool for propping open a window, or as fuel for a fire, or as a means of defending ourselves in an attack. A pencil is a pencil. It is not a combination of graphite, wood, brass and rubber, each of which have multiple properties and multiples uses."

You can use this test as a game to play with friends. A group can stir up an avalanche of ideas.

#1: KINDRED RELATIONS

Answers: 1. Bed. 2. Blue. 3. Red. 4. Soft. 5. Money. 6. Fruit. 7. Band. 8. Star. 9. Sweet. 10. Blind. 11. Cat. 12. Bed. 13. French. 14. Soap. 15. Bird. 16. Chicken. 17. Social. 18. Cold. 19. Moon. 20. Monkey. 21. Hell. 22. Dog. 23. Pigeon. 24. Chicken. 25. Black. 26. Wise. 27. Big. 28. Business. 29. Egg. 30. Evening. 31. Head. 32. Character. 33. Close. 34. Yellow. 35. Vitamin. 36. Sign. 37. Morning. 38. Jump. 39. Cow. 40. Cock. 41. Middle. 42. Leave.

#2: CONCEALED COLORS

Answers: 1. Gold. 2. Copper. 3. Olive. 4. Tan. 5. Yellow. 6. Lavender. 7. Gray. 8. Lilac. 9. Silver. 10. White. 11. Pearly. 12. Chrome. 13. Fawn. 14. Brown. 15. Chestnut. 16. Scarlet. 17. Ochre. 18. Pink. 19. Green. 20. Orange. 21. Indigo.

In order to identify the "hidden colors," you have to disregard the signs that say "stop"—such as word spacings, periods, and commas. Some people who are very habit-ridden find this exercise difficult to do.

#3: TELL A STORY

Example: A broken cane. A broken crutch.

A beggar whom people thought was blind and who used a heavy cane to get about, always used the same spot near a big church to beg for money. He was very fond of this particular place, for he found that people coming from the church—particularly on Sundays—were very generous with their alms. And so he came to regard this spot as his private territory.

One Sunday morning, as he was approaching his spot near the church, he noticed that a cripple on crutches was occupying it. He told the cripple to move to a different place, but the cripple refused. Angered by this, he raised his cane and started beating the beggar. People passing by were startled to see the "blind" man wield his cane with such uncanny precision and the cripple's nimble dodging of the "blind" man's blows. The "blind" man finally broke his cane, but also managed to wrest a crutch from the "cripple," which he then broke in two across his knee.

Having been found out, they decided to join forces and move to a different part of town, where they shared the spot near a church at different times of the day. They also switched roles: the "blind" beggar became the cripple and the "cripple" the blind man.

#4: THE FRUGAL WOMAN

Sample ideas:
1. She just won a great deal of money on a lottery ticket.
2. She inherited a fortune from her tight-fisted husband who never let her spend money on luxuries.
3. She has just learned from her doctor that she has only a few more months to live.
4. She found a map leading to buried loot gangsters had hidden in her yard.
5. She learned that inflation was increasing so rapidly that her money would be worthless in six months.
6. Her psychiatrist has convinced her that her frugal habits stem from a very austere, strict, and overly disciplined childhood.
7. Her husband has found another woman. To get even, she is spending money freely.
8. She left a religious sect that had required a vow of poverty.
9. She discovered that her only relatives were planning to kill her for her money.
10. She suddenly became senile.
11. She learned that her money was all counterfeit, and that the FBI was about to confiscate it.
12. She has successfully completed plastic surgery, and she decided to get a completely new wardrobe to go with her rejuvenated appearance.

#5: LOOSE ENDS

Most people will see the difficulty as a shortness of reach: that is, they state the problem to themselves as "How can I get to the second string?" The consequence of this is that all the creative effort goes into vain efforts to find a means of making one of the strings longer. But the "givens" of this problem make such a solution impossible.

If, however, you define the problem as "How can the string and I get together?", another sort of solution may well occur to you. The solution requires that you see the difficulty in terms of getting the second string to come to *you.* If you tie a small object —say, a key or a ring—to the end of one string and set it swinging like a pendulum, then you can grab it while still holding the end of the second string in the other hand.

#6: SHORT SUCCINCT SENTENCES

Examples: "B"

Butter burnt bread. Beat bad boys. Bandits betray brothers. Backgammon beats bridge. Bananas boil badly. Black bears bite. Bullion boom busts. Bake brown bread. Backward blustering bosses. Bulletin boards banned. Buoyant boats bump. Burp bottle babies. Blind beggar's blues. Brash brats bluster. Etc.

"T"

Taffy tastes terrible. Tailors tie threads. Trampling tears taffeta. Tall tables totter. Tired teachers tremble. Twist turtles' tails. Thieves terrorize town. Thin tigers trapped. Timid Timothy thinks. Tongue twister tests. Trousers trip tenor. Tom thinks thin. Tourists' trifling tips. Town's thunderous tribute. Trust true togetherness. Tender tempestuous types. Etc.

#7: SAFETY DRIVE

Examples: 1. Give money prizes for those with least traffic violations. 2. Pass stricter laws and have better enforcement of those laws. 3. Reduce the horsepower of cars. 4. Do more research on "crashproof" cars. 5. Newspapers should feature more photographs of car accidents. 6. Have separate roads for buses, cars, bicycles, etc. 7. Impose ambulance and/or clinic duty on offenders. 8. Have special racetracks where drivers may rid themselves of aggression. 9. Give psychological instruction as early as possible in childhood to condition children to the proper use of car. 10. Install electric guidance systems. 11. Put governors on cars to prevent them from exceeding 50 miles per hour. 12. All drivers should be forced to pass psychological and coordination tests. 13. Install buzzers in cars that are activated when speeds exceed 55 miles per hour. 14. Install breathalizers in cars which prevent them from being started when the person is intoxicated. 15. Encourage greater use of mass transportation systems. 16. Install blinking lights on the dashboard that indicate excessive speed. 17. Use a radar system that keeps cars away from each other. 18. At every 300-400 feet have bumps in the road that will force the cars to slow down. 19. Eliminate installment buying of cars. 20. Have cars ride on tracks. 21. Prohibit passing. 22. Have cars painted in colors that are more visible at night. 23. Raise income-tax levies on traffic violators. 24. Make it mandatory to wear seat belts. 25. Raise the minimum-age requirement for driver's license. 26. Stagger working hours to reduce traffic. 27. Put governors on trucks and buses to slow them down. 28. Encourage the use of car pools. 29. Limit the number of cars per family. 30. Increase the number of traffic policemen. 31. Increase fines for violations. 32. Conduct more effective campaigns for safe driving. 33. Outlaw cars in cities. 34. Make mass transportation free. 35. Improve the sound of horns: make them musical. 36. Increase the quality and comfort of buses and trains: have piped-in music and stewardesses serving drinks. 37. Equip cars with flexible windows that will bend on impact. 38. Replace present engines with battery-operated engines. 39. Develop psychological tests to determine whether prospective driver has suicidal or homicidal tendencies. 40. Install new traffic lights that cast a tremendous glare. 41. Require the driver who kills someone to pay funeral expenses and support the victim's family for the rest of their lives. Etc.

If you had trouble coming up with the required number of ideas in the time frame we set, you probably made some premature judgments.

At the end of a brainstorming session, when evaluation is finally applied, it is often one of the most apparently silly ideas that points the way to a solution. For example, in one brainstorming session, as reported by Alex F. Osborn, the father of the "brainstorming" technique, the following problem was posed to the participants:

"If 700 miles of outside telephone wires were coated with three inches of frost so that long-distance calls could not be made, how would you restore normal service as fast as possible?"

In fifteen minutes, over twenty possible solutions were given. Among them were:

1. Charge the wire with a heat-building current that would melt the frost off.
2. Put smudge pots or fires on ground beneath wires.

3. Use flame throwers or blowtorches.
4. Have crews knock off with long poles.
5. Use infrared heat units to defrost wires.
6. Have a helicopter fly over so that its downdraft would melt the ice.

This last idea met with laughter. And yet, when that same problem actually developed in the Northwest a few months later, the helicopter solution actually turned out to be the best solution.

#8: TAKE A GOOD LOOK

Examples:
"You're right, the aspirin didn't dissolve."
"Of course, your Blue Cross would pay for an X ray."
"When I asked you to take a deep breath, I never . . ."
"Doctor, I think I'm getting lockjaw."
"You haven't been following the diet I prescribed."
"Your shoelaces are untied."
"I thought I asked you to remove your dentures."
"I can never remember which are the stalagmites."
"I'm stuck!"
"Can't take any more chances with all those malpractice suits."
"You're right, you do have butterflies."
"In my entire medical practice, I never . . ."
"This will only take a minute."
"Doctor, you're stepping on my toes."
"Nurse, the syringe please."

Most of the sample captions supplied support the exaggeration by suggesting that the doctor could actually *see* something from his unique vantage point. Conceiving of the patient's inner space in terms of a simile—"It's like a cave"—brings to mind bats and limestone formations. You did fine if your captions similarly extended or enlarged on this game of make-believe.

#9: MEDICAL EMERGENCY

The answer, of course, is that the surgeon is the boy's mother. Although there are many women doctors—and many of them prominent specialists—our cultural stereotyping tells us that doctors are men and nurses are women. It is worth noting that the story might just as easily have been about a nurse attending the patient because most large hospitals now have a substantial number of male nurses. The identification of a profession with a particular sex is diminishing gradually, to the great benefit of coming generations.

In a similar but much earlier story, two Indians—a tall one and a short one—arrive at a military post to negotiate with U.S. marshals about the land that the Indians are occupying. They look very much alike, and in fact, they are closely related. The short Indian is the son of the tall Indian, but the tall Indian is not the father of the short Indian. What is their relationship? Beware of sexual stereotyping.

#10: DIAMONDS AND RUBIES

If you used vertical thinking, you probably arrived at these three unattractive possibilities:
1. The princess should refuse to take the stone.
2. The princess should show that there are two rubies in the jewelry box, and expose the queen's trickery.
3. The princess should take one of the rubies and sacrifice her happiness.

One lateral-thinking solution to this problem is this:

The princess put her hand into the jewelry box and drew out a stone. Without showing it to others or looking at it, she let it fall to the path where it got lost among the other precious stones.

"How stupid of me," she exclaimed, "but if you look in the jewelry box, you can easily determine which stone I picked by the one that remained."

There are other lateral solutions possible:

The princess could say to the prince: "Since you want to marry me, please do the drawing for me. Remove one of the jewels, show it to us, and I shall be content with the one that remains."

The princess could drop her handkerchief, and while picking it up, palm a diamond. Then, when inserting her hand in the jewelry box, she could come out with the diamond.

She calls the queen's attention to an object in the sky, and as the queen searches for it, she picks up two diamonds and substitutes them for the rubies.

She stumbles against the queen and causes the jewelry box to fall on the ground. While picking it up, she lets the rubies out and replaces them with the diamonds.

She tells the queen that the prince has a very contagious disease which she has already contracted.

She advises the queen that she is pregnant by the prince.

Neither vertical or lateral thinking is to be used to the exclusion of the other, but they should be employed alternately. Lateral thinking is most useful when the vertical or consecutive thinking has taken you to a dead end.

With many problems, the ability to "shift gears" from one form of thinking to the other greatly increases the chances that you will arrive at a correct and creative solution.

#11: BREAKING OUT

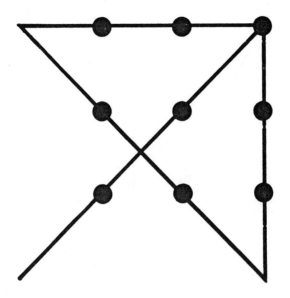

This puzzle is a perfect illustration of how "rules" and "restrictions" that we carry with us unconsciously can inhibit problem-solving and why most people can not exceed the imaginary square-shaped boundary. (Note that the restriction of the boundary was not part of the problem as posed.)

When they first begin coloring with crayons, children often go beyond the lines of the figures. Of course, this is partly because they lack manual control. But it may also be because they are not yet intimidated by boundaries—either real or imaginary. With adults, unfortunately, the desire to conform fences them in.

Researchers at Stanford University have come up with an even more astounding solution to this puzzle. One subject realized that it wasn't necessary to draw four lines through the centers of the dots; it can be accomplished with only three lines:

And if that weren't enough, a friend of Professor James L. Adams of Stanford University provided an absolutely fantastic solution, which allows all nine dots to be crossed off by one straight line. All it requires is a little unblocked and ingenious paper folding.

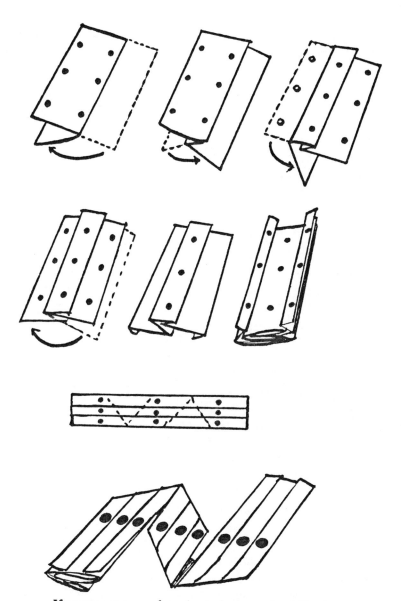

If you want to see how it works, copy the following pages and follow directions.

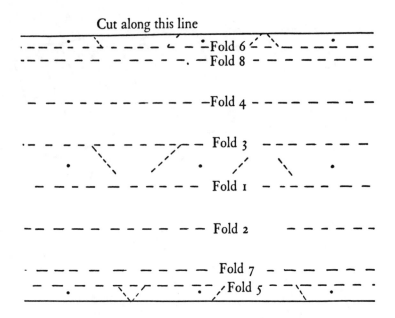

Cut along this line

Fold 6
Fold 8
Fold 4
Fold 3
Fold 1
Fold 2
Fold 7
Fold 5

#12: BRIDGE THE GAPS

Examples:

1. Star   light   day   long   before
2. Lemon   yellow   paint   house   dog
3. Fire   escape   fast   run   scared
4. Dog   tag   laundry   wash   white
5. Postage   stamp   foot   sore   knee
6. White   wash   clean   face   about
7. Short   fall   down   cast   out
8. Blood   test   paper   white   color
9. Light   cigarette   smoke   screen   test
10. Blue   sky   high   jump   ball
11. Hunt   man   gun   fire   house
12. Cat   house   light   load   car
13. Sleep   sound   sour   taste   bad
14. Concert   piano   practice   teaching   machine
15. Puppy   love   sick   leave   home

These series of small, conceptual steps are *examples only.* You may have found different and equally valid steps of your own.

This exercise required that you identify the steps you take in arriving at solutions. Some problems requiring a creative solution consist of a problem situation and a goal. The steps toward reaching the goal are not immediately apparent and require that you exercise your creativity. In a way, it is like building a bridge, each section of which must be linked carefully, to the section preceding and following it.

#13: THE MIND'S EYE

Examples of responses: 1. A woman cuddling and rocking a screaming baby. 2. A word written in Oriental language. 3. A girl carrying a surfboard. 4. A smiling witch's head flying through the air. 5. A little man with horns and tail, flying on a gigantic bird. 6. A skunk on a skiboard. 7. Profile of someone in a car; scarf flying in the wind. 8. Dancer taking a leap. 9. A tubular plant with a new shoot. 10. Curled ribbon on a package. 11. Letters "V" and "Y". 12. A wishbone. 13. A person exercising. 14. A sign in mathematics. 15. Sewage washing into water. 16. An old fogey reading a heavy book. 17. Waves. 18. A dancer. 19. Pair of pliers or shears. 20. A very sneaky fish. 21. A small dog sliding down a board. 22. Something flying in the air. 23. A flower or a plant. 24. Head and two legs.

1. Windowpane with a hole in it. 2. A tired, battle-scarred Russian soldier resting on a snowbank. 3. Profile of a Norseman. 4. A soldier with firecrackers coming out of his head. 5. A smiling woman's profile with a fancy hairdo. 6. A dog lying on a log. 7. A flying squirrel. 8. Grasshopper. 9. Root of a tree. 10.

An Irish setter jumping. 11. Horse's head. 12. A wolf's head. 13. Cliffs with a stone tower. 14. A castle in a forest. 15. A castle on top of a hill. 16. Roses and tulips. 17. Water splashing. 18. Faraway castles. 19. Face of a poodle. 20. A rock. 21. Tops of trees in a distance.

There are basically three "measures" that distinguish the more creative individuals from the less creative.

First, the more creative individuals tend to see something in the whole, or the major portion of the blots, while the less creative individuals see fewer wholes and concentrate on small portions or details of the blots. The more creative individuals want to achieve the most difficult and far-reaching ordering of the inkblot, taking account of all details in one comprehensive image.

Second, the more creative individuals see some movement, action, something going on in the figures (they frequently tell a story about what is going on), while the less creative individuals see more static things and figures. When the more creative individuals see something static, they are more descriptive and detailed in their responses.

Third, the more creative individuals give more original, imaginative, and uncommon responses to the formless blots.

#14: SIMPLE ARITHMETIC

If you dealt with it sequentially as a series of unrelated problems, you probably didn't get very far because you had to retranslate the terms for each one.

The secret is to do all the addition problems first, then go back and do all the division problems, and so on. That eliminates the need for constantly referring back to the "code." Approaching it this way, many people can complete *all* the problems in one minute.

#15: **MAKE SOMETHING OF IT**

Examples:

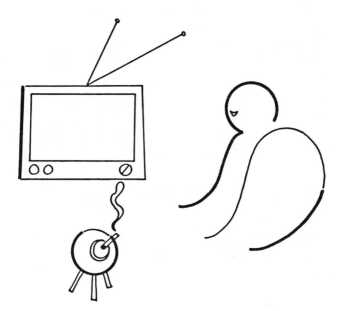

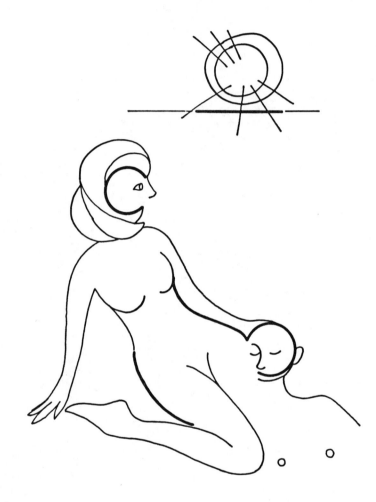

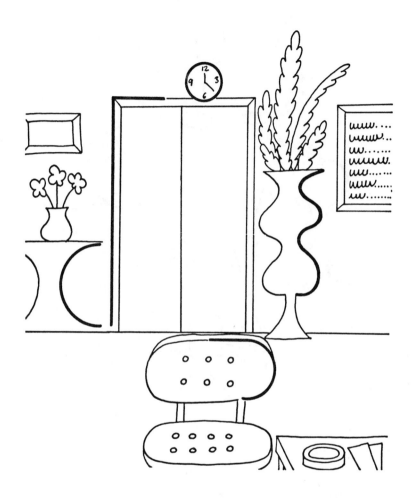

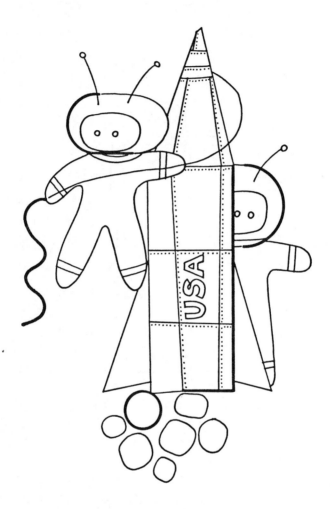

#16: BRIGHT BUT SHY

Examples:

1. Brighter individuals are more aware of what they do not know and therefore experience feelings of inadequacy.

2. Brighter individuals might have felt more inadequate to

begin with and therefore compensated for this by becoming brighter.

3. Brighter individuals lack skill in sports and social affairs, and since these attributes are culturally valued, they tend to develop feelings of inferiority.

4. Brighter individuals are more introverted and taciturn than are extroverted individuals and they do not get the attention that the extroverted individuals do. Hence they tend to develop feelings of inadequacy.

5. Brighter individuals are more perceptive and aware and thus are more pessimistic about things in general. This generates feelings of helplessness and inadequacy.

6. Brighter individuals have trouble in making their thinking understood, so often feel inadequate.

#17: THE COLLECTED WORKS

Five inches.

If you had trouble with this one, you were probably trapped by a habitual way of visualizing. All our lives we've been accustomed to seeing a book in a certain position—facing us, with the first page near the left-hand cover and the last page nearest the right-hand cover. That is the way we prepare to open a book and read. But we specified in this problem that the volumes were on the shelf, and even gave you a graphic illustration to orient you. With the backs facing you, the order of pages is reversed.

In creative problem-solving it serves well to heed the rule: The more familiar the object, the harder it is to see it in another context.

#18: MANY MEANINGS

Examples: Skillful, intelligent, ingenious, quick-witted, shrewd, smart, keen, brilliant, proficient, crafty, sagacious, sharp, inventive, capable, quick, resourceful, good at, skilled, efficient, endowed, cunning, up to snuff, acute, perspicacious, discerning, brainy, bright, sharp-witted, astute, penetrating, intellectual, knowing, to have the smarts, hip, wise-guy, with it, smarty-pants, adroit, dexterous, witty, facile, nimble-witted, expert, competent, accomplished, talented, able, gifted, apt, slick, deft, up to, at home in, master of, a good hand at, masterly, conversant, up to the mark, sure-footed, eagle-eyed, wise, quick of apprehension, canny, farsighted, sharp as a needle, alive to, cool, profound, prudent, politic, wise, expedient, well-contrived, smart aleck, etc.

#19: WHAT WOULD HAPPEN IF—I

Examples:
   1. New naming systems would have to be devised to identify parentage.

2. Wills and other legal documents would become more complicated.
3. The oldest profession would be in danger of going out of business.
4. There would be fewer childless families.
5. There would no longer be any need for sequential marriages.
6. Houses would have to be bigger.
7. Legal residences would be hard to establish.
8. Child support would have to be assured by some other system.
9. Feelings of jealousy would eventually lessen.
10. Record bureaus would either disappear or become a major industry.
11. The polygamous "instincts" of many men and women would find free expression.
12. Some people wouldn't be able to adapt to this arrangement; others would welcome it.

#20: HALF OF THIRTEEN

There are seven answers: 1, 2, 3, 4, 6.5, 8, and 11.
Half of thirteen is 6.5; 1/3 gives you 1 and 3; thir/teen gives you 4, and ~~XIII~~ produces 8. XI/II gives you 2 and 11.

In creative problem-solving, it is frequently more important to look at a problem from different vantage points rather than run with the first solution that pops into mind.

#21: FUN WITH PUNS

Illegal	—	sick bird
Parole	—	the father role (function)
Hydrophobia	—	fear of falling from high places
Armature	—	limb of a grown man

Kidnap	—	child sleeping; goat sleeping
Curtail	—	tail of an animal; bitter beer; short story; short illness
Overtired	—	seven tires on a car; outwardly angry
Therapist	—	a man who rapes
Kindred	—	fear of relatives; generous color
Ferocity	—	city of iron; Egyptian city; city of pharaohs; fear of city; city plowed up; where gophers live.

According to the famous author Arthur Koestler, "The creative process entails—in science, humor, and art—a kind of punning procedure in which disparates are fused." Koestler also observed, "The poetic rhyme is nothing but a glorified pun: two strings of ideas tied in an acoustic knot." Koestler feels that punning involves a temporary, but voluntary and healthy regression in the service of the ego. In his words: "The capacity to regress, more or less at will, to the games of the underground, without losing contact with the surface, seems to be the essence of the poetic, and of any other form of creativity."

The genius of the Marx Brothers' humor was almost entirely based on their punning ability. In one of their movies, Chico Marx mistakes the word "taxes" for "Texas," and then proceeds to "define" "taxes" as "dollars": "Thatsa right—I gotta uncle that lives in Dollahs. Dollahs, Taxes." Chico's Italian accent enabled him to use a continuous flow of puns: "You got a haddock? I gotta haddock too. Whatta you take for a haddock?" Or "Sturgeon. Sturgeon. Thatsa doctor thatta cuts you up."

Punning is sometimes reputed to be a low form of humor—mostly by those who haven't the skill or are too inhibited to engage in it. Good punning is actually quite difficult, and some erudite souls engage in multilingual punning of a very sophisticated sort.

The beauty of the "Dollahs, Taxes" example is that it is an ingenious circular pun, which returns to the starting point.

#22: COME AS YOU ARE

Examples:

1. Borrow clothes from a friend who is roughly the same size.
2. Wear your wife's dress and a wig and tell the host you thought it was a costume party.
3. Find an all-night formal-wear place and rent a tuxedo.
4. Switch the party to your house and ask each of the other guests to bring one article of clothing in your size.
5. Borrow clothes from one of the firemen who came to put out the fire.
6. Use bedsheets or curtains to improvise a togalike garment. Explain to the hostess that you attended a costume party and didn't have time to change clothing.
7. Ask the host to call all the guests and tell them it's to be a "come-as-you-are" party. Guests are required to come dressed as they were when they received the invitation. You could then go in a bathrobe.
8. Call the host's caterer and ask him to send a uniform in your size.

#23: SHORT DEFINITIONS

Examples:

1. Patience: "A minor form of despair, disguised as virtue."—Ambrose Bierce
2. Hope: "A pathological belief in the occurrence of the impossible."—H. L. Mencken
3. A Pastor: "One employed by the wicked to prove to them by his example that virtue doesn't pay."—H. L. Mencken
4. A Politician: "An animal who can sit on a fence and yet keep both ears to the ground."—Oscar Wilde
5. An Expert: "An ordinary man away from home giving advice."—Oscar Wilde
6. A weed: "A plant whose virtues have not been discovered." —Ralph Waldo Emerson

7. A grapefruit: "A lemon that had a chance and took advantage of it."—Oscar Wilde
8. Revolution: "In politics, an abrupt change in the form of misgovernment."—Ambrose Bierce

If you're not satisfied with what you came up with, go back, and this time try your skill in competing with what the above past masters at aphoristic definitions produced.

#24: WHAT GOES DOWN, BUT WON'T GO UP?

The traditional answer is that the man is a dwarf or a midget, and cannot reach the top button. It might also, of course, be a man who is confined to a wheelchair or who has some other physical limitation that restricts his movement.

But consider some other possibilities that might account for his behavior. For example:

1. He has a sick friend living on the twentieth floor whom he visits every night before going home.
2. He lives in a duplex apartment that occupies two floors. Thus he leaves from his bedroom on the twenty-second floor, and returns to his kitchen and living room on the floor below.
3. A habitual drinker, he arrives home late at night. Not wanting to awaken his wife with the sound of the elevator doors, he gets off on the twenty-first floor and walks up the stairs.
4. He is following an exercise program that requires him to climb a specified number of flights of steps each day.
5. There is a restaurant at the nineteenth floor and he stops there every night to have a few "bracers" before facing his wife.
6. He has a mistress living on the twenty-first floor and he visits with her before going home.

7. In the past, the elevator has frequently gotten stuck between the twenty-first and the twenty-second floor. To avoid this, he gets off on the twentieth floor and walks up.

8. He doesn't like his apartment and in order to prolong his arrival there, he gets off on the tenth floor and walks up.

9. He is a go-getter. His wife works for a family on the nineteenth floor and every night, after a full day of job-hunting, he has to go and get her.

10. His tympanic cavities are badly inflamed, and he has to walk up slowly several flights to get used to the altitude.

#25: A WOMAN'S INGENUITY

As long as you think of the segments of chain as four sides of a square, or segments of a circle, you can't solve this problem. The moment you can shift your focus and regard one of those segments—not as an immutable structure—but as a stockpile of individual links, you've made the necessary "breakthrough." At the woman's suggestion, the jeweler placed three segments in a triangular pattern, took apart the remaining segment, and used those three links to close the three corners of the necklace.

Most people will need to juggle the elements visually, drawing them in different arrangements before arriving at the triangular pattern that leads to solution. This playful juggling of the parts of a problem results in a reorganization—but before that can happen, you have to feel free to destroy the original pattern of systematic arrangement in which the problem was presented.

INTERMEDIATE TEST A: MONEY . . . MONEY . . . MONEY

Examples: 1. Use as decoration (on handbags, shoes, sweaters, etc.). 2. Use for gambling. 3. To draw circles. 4. Buy things. 5. To stop up sink. 6. Collect as a hobby. 7. Teach small children how to count. 8. Throw in fountains for good luck. 9. Save. 10. To pry open cans, jars, etc. 11. Use as pressure object to stop bleeding, swelling. 12. Hide in mattress. 13. Swallow to get sick. 14. Make necklace, earrings, bracelet. 15. Make objects (pictures, mobiles, etc.). 16. Give to beggars. 17. Use as emblem for banks, money-lending institutions. 18. Sell to coin collectors. 19. To play checkers. 20. Make rattles. 21. Make eyes, noses for dolls, stuffed animals, snowmen, etc. 22. Melt down for silver, copper, etc. 23. Use as a slug. 24. Use as a small target. 25. Suck or chew on. 26. Use as a play monocle. 27. Jingle in the pocket to impress date. 28. Play with when nervous. 29. Hide tear or spot (on dress). 30. Make clip to hold paper money. 31. Steal from parking meters. 32. Use as a watch face. 33. Give away to win affection. 34. Flip to see who starts a game. 35. As paperweight. 36. Tie or glue a string on and wing to scare flies, birds, etc. 37. Use in magic. 38. Construct pendulum. 39. Put texture on paintings. 40. Reflect sunlight. 41. Teething for babies. 42. Drop to annoy people. 43. Christmas tree decoration. 44. Collect for historical value. 45. Stuff dolls. 46. Embed in walks. 47. Throw in shallow pond for color. 48. As wheels on a toy car. 49. As lid on a small jar. 50. As eyes in gingerbread cookies. 51. Tie on a string for cat to play with. 52. Throw in water for diving practice. Etc. etc.

If you did the previous games and exercises conscientiously, you should already be able to produce a greater number of possible uses than you did on the pre-test.

#26: HOW HEADLINES HAPPEN

Examples:
  1. Southern Senator's Staunch Stand
  2. Secret Service Spy Sings
  3. Surgeon's Scalpel Saves Syrian
  4. Singer's Sudden Success Story
  5. Statistics Show Suicides Slipping
  6. Suburb Swingers' Shady Shenanigans
  7. Swanky Swede's Swan Song
  8. Supermarket's Surplus Sale Slow
  9. Supplementary Sums Supplied Soon
  10. Super Star's Supreme Sacrifice
  11. Ships Sail Suez Slowly
  12. Summer School Starts Sunday

#27: LEAD PARAGRAPH

Example: Stolen Stradivarius Still Sought
  New York police continue to exhaust every lead and tip in an effort to find Jascha Heifetz's second-best Stradivarius, recently taken by the notorious "catgut burglar." "I always kept it hidden either in the bread box or in the old steamer trunk I use as a coffee table," said Heifetz, interviewed in the bathtub in his small but chic Greenwich Village apartment.

#28: HOSPITAL'S BONANZA

Sample ideas:

1. They organized the fete for the spring and had a large turn-out of people from the community.
2. The volunteers working for this fete started preparations early and they did a door-to-door campaign, which ensured a large turnout.
3. Instead of just one car, as in previous years, the hospital decided to raffle off five cars, donated by the local car dealers, and found that they had sold ten times as many tickets as in previous years.
4. The local merchants of the community contributed more free merchandise to be sold at the fete.
5. To encourage charitable giving, the IRS offered double deductions for hospital contributions and for things purchased at the fete.
6. They were lucky to secure the free services of some top entertainers in the country who drew a large crowd not only from the community, but also from other nearby towns.
7. The local radio station and newspapers gave them more publicity, starting two months prior to the fete.
8. The hospital was in real danger of going bankrupt, and the populace in the community decided to come to the rescue.
9. The hospital arranged free diabetes and high-blood-pressure tests at the fete, and this brought out more people.
10. The volunteers succeeded in obtaining expensive antiques for auctioning off.
11. The hospital announced that only those families who made a contribution—no matter how modest—would have access to emergency services.
12. The hospital arranged a circus and more amusements for the children, thus attracting more parents.
13. The hospital arranged to have the famous surgeon, Dr. Christopher Arebutnot to autograph his latest book at the fete.

14. A local millionaire agreed to match each contribution, dollar for dollar.
15. Oil was discovered in the community, and most families became wealthy when they sold the rights to their land.

#29: IT'S IN THE BAG

He reached into his pocket, extracted a book of matches, lit one and set fire to the bag. When the bag had burned to ashes, he selected an iron, swung, and watched the ball roll to the rim of the hole. Unable to get the ball away from the paper bag without a penalty, this golfer was imaginative enough to recognize that the problem could be solved by getting the paper bag away from the ball.

The "reversal" of problems, the "purging" of habitual, accepted, or established ways of thinking about things has brought many important advances.

#30: THE SHIPWRECKED SAILOR

Other possible solutions:
1. When his ship sank, he had noticed that a long coral reef was jutting out just below the surface a couple of miles from the island.

On the appointed day, he directed the crew to paddle close to the reef. He told the sorcerer that he had to perform a ritual in the boat before stepping out—actually waiting for the low tide to arrive.

Finally, when he saw the reef emerging, he stepped out and merrily hop-skipped across it.

2. In his travels to far-distant corners of the world he had learned the art of hypnotism. During his week's stay he had noticed that the natives were easily hypnotized.

When the boat was a few miles out, he asked to perform a

ceremony, which he used to put everybody in a deep trance. He suggested to them that when he would repeat the word "Umbanda" three times, they would see him walking on the water. The experiment succeeded, and he lived happily ever after.

3. He told the sorcerer that not only could he walk on the water, but that he had the "power" to give this ability to the sorcerer and the rest of the tribe. The only thing was that they all had to tie a "magic" stone to their feet.

When they were a couple of miles out, the natives were anxious to try out their promised prowess. Naturally, with the heavy stones tied to their feet, they all sank to the bottom. The sailor returned to the island, where he had hidden the beautiful sorcerer's daughter. Soon he had an heir to his throne.

4. He had saved some explosives, kerosene, timing devices, etc., from the ship that had been washed ashore, and he carried these to the mouth of the volcano during the night.

He told the sorcerer that walking on water was really no "miracle" for him, but that he could make the volcano erupt at command and then stop it at will.

The volcano had a special significance for the tribe, for it had twice nearly destroyed the island. The sorcerer agreed that this would be an even stronger proof that he was their "god."

The next day, after the tribe had gathered on the beach, he performed his ceremony, then stepped on a device he had hidden in the sand. This set off a chain-reaction of explosions and fireworks from the volcano. The sorcerer and the natives watched the spectacle with great amazement and awe. After it subsided, they carried the sailor to the throne and his godhood was never again challenged.

5. He told the sorcerer that breathing underwater would be a far greater miracle than walking on top of it. He then dove in, swam underwater to the nearby wreckage of his ship, entered the hull through an underwater hole, and hid for an hour before emerging to wild acclaim.

#31: NEW DIRECTIONS

You may well have done better than the professional designers did, but here are their solutions:

1. Lost and Found

2. Hotel Information

Gloves and umbrellas are simple to depict in silhouette, and are, perhaps, the most commonly lost items. Note that the question mark used in the information sign is repeated here. The end result: glove and umbrella information, or lost and found.

Hotel information is handled similarly. A stylized or stick figure is shown in a bed, which, after all, is what hotels are all about, and the information symbol also appears.

The customs inspector symbol depends largely on the white waist and chest belt, which is a common symbol of authority in both Europe and in Asia. It is less familiar in the United States, but is sometimes worn by military police and school-crossing guards.

#32: THE ROYAL WIZARD

Examples:
1. The Logical Flaw
2. A Costly Oversight
3. Miscalculation
4. The Limits of Wisdom
5. The Easy Way Out

6. His Wit's End
7. The Genius Gap
8. The Last Alternative
9. The Witless Wiseman
10. Chinese King—Foo Ling Yoo

In general, titles that show freshness, surprise, and humor are rated as more creative and original responses.

#33: OF LOVE AND LIVING

Here are some notable observations on the subject of "life" that may give you some inspiration.

1. "Life is a short interval between birth and death, and our task is to make the most of it."
2. "Life is a hearty breakfast and a skimpy supper."
3. "Life is the art of drawing sufficient conclusions from insufficient premises."—Samuel Butler
4. "Life is a hospital in which every patient is possessed by the desire of changing his bed."—Charles P. Baudelaire
5. "Life is like playing a violin solo in public and learning the instrument as one goes on."—Samuel Butler
6. "Life is not a spectacle or a feast; it is a predicament."— George Santayana
7. "Life is a glorious cycle of song, a medley of extemporanea." —Dorothy Parker
8. "Life is like a tale ended before it's told."—T. B. Aldrich
9. "Life is a train of moods, like a string of beads."—Ralph Waldo Emerson.

The use of metaphors is not limited to any one field of endeavor. It is no exaggeration to say that poetry, literature, and the arts could not exist without metaphors. Without metaphors, they could not communicate the relationships, the "qualitative kinships" that exist between things.

141

It has also been recognized that in science and technology, it is frequently a metaphor or analogy which provides the key to a new invention, a new theory, or the solution to a difficult problem. For example, the following inventions were all based on metaphorical thought, associations, or connections: Archimedes's law of gravity and hydrostatics; Gutenberg's movable type; Kepler's operational theory of celestial mechanics; Harvey's concept of the circulation of the blood; James Watt's steam engine; Benjamin Franklin's lightning rod; and many others.

#34: THE GREEK CROSS

This problem can only be solved one coin from the right arm to the left arm and move the extra coin at the bottom to a position on top of the center coin:

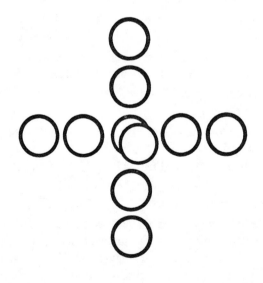

"Not fair," you say? Sure it is. There is nothing in the directions as given that prevents you from working in more than two dimensions. In most problems of this kind, the solution involves *sliding* the coins from one position to another. This problem illustrates how hard it is to break out of the usual or common ways of problem-solving—and how easy it is to read into a problem constraints that are not there at all.

We gave a similar problem to participants in a creative problem-solving workshop and even, in spite of the broad hint we provided in the title of the exercise, *The New Pyramid*, the majority of the participants failed to solve it. See if you can do better.

Using six kitchen matches, make *four* equilateral triangles out of these *six* matches.

Most participants began by using three matches to form one triangle, and then tried in vain to form three more from the remaining three matches.

This problem can only be solved by using the third dimension. Three matches can be used to build a triangle on the table, and the remaining three to build a pyramid with the initial triangle as a base.

Lack of flexibility in moving from one dimension to another has been demonstrated by several experiments, among them this simple but ingenious problem-solving experiment:

A group of individuals was presented with the task of extracting a Ping-Pong ball from a long and narrow cylinder, which was bolted to the floor. A great variety of tools, including a hammer, pliers, piece of string, thumbtacks, and so on were laid out. None of these was applicable for the solution of the problem. There was, however, also a bucket of dirty water standing on the floor. About half of the individuals present finally got the idea that the Ping-Pong ball could be extracted by filling the cylinder with the water.

Another group of individuals was presented the same problem. The tools were all there, but the bucket with dirty water was missing. Instead, a table nearby was set with china and silver, as if for a banquet, and in the center was a large pitcher with water and ice cubes in it. Only a few individuals in this group were able to solve the problem. The majority were unable to break through the barrier separating the world of dining from the world of mechanical problems and mechanical tools.

#35: A MILITARY TALE

People usually make something of these lines: the bare branches of a windblown tree, a part of a street map, a sketch of a tool, or part of a circuit diagram.

If you solved the doodle easily, you probably recognized first that the vertical line represented the edge of an opaque structure concealing most of the other elements of the drawing. It is, in fact, a wall.

The purported story surrounding this drawing is this: A young man had a dog that was very fond of him. When the man entered the army, the dog went along—following his master everywhere.

On this occasion, the young soldier was walking his post on sentry duty with the dog at his heels. What you see is the bayonet on the rifle, and the tail of the dog after the soldier has turned the corner of the building. The story, as you can see, transforms the lines into a new structure.

#36: S C A M S

Examples:
1. Sleepy cats always move slowly.
2. Singing cellos alter mood substantially.
3. Sabotage caused army's moves southward.
4. Spoiled children angered mother steadily.
5. Straightened circumstances affect man's stability.
6. Strike caused austerity moves subsequently.
7. School classes appear moderately satisfying.
8. Studious children always merit success.
9. Sly crocodiles attacked migrating settlers.
10. Siamese cats age much slower.
11. Store closes after Monday's shoplifting.
12. Sculptor created a monument speedily.
13. Swimming can affect muscular strength.

14. Senegal's citizen a murder suspect.
15. Success comes after much study.
16. Southern China attacks Mongolian stronghold.
17. Sinister character alarms Manhattan's strollers.
18. Some citizens are moderately successful.
19. Symphony created attractive musical sounds.
20. Swaggering Chinese angered many strollers.

#37: NATURE'S INVENTIONS

Answers:

1.	Bat	(15)	Snowshoes
2.	Armadillo	(16)	Swaddling clothes
3.	Chameleon	(1)	Sonar
4.	Deep-sea fishes	(14)	Gun blasts and chemical attack
5.	Echidna	(2)	Tank
6.	Squid	(3)	Camouflage
7.	Flying squirrel	(13)	Suction cup
8.	Hummingbird	(11)	Anesthesia
9.	Birds	(4)	Electricity
10.	Scorpion	(8)	Helicopter
11.	Snake	(5)	Spurs
12.	Antelope	(7)	Parachute
13.	Abalone	(6)	Jet propulsion
14.	Beetle	(10)	Hypodermic
15.	Caribou	(12)	Signal code
16.	Silkworm	(9)	Plane flaps (for braking)

1. The bat used sonar long before it was discovered. As it flies, it emits a series of sharp cries unheard to the human ear but audible to itself. As the cries bounce off various objects, they warn the bat of the approach of obstructions. In experiments,

blindfolded bats could still fly perfectly, but bats with their ears plugged up flew into something at once.

2. Both armadillo and turtle antedate the tank.

3. Before modern warfare invented it, the chameleon was a master of camouflage. It can rapidly change its color from green to yellow and gray.

4. Some deep-sea fish have their own electric plants. They are equipped with electric stingers, with lighted "portholes" along their bodies and lanterns in their jaws or on their tails. Many—the electric eel particularly—have electric "batteries" strong enough to deliver a lethal shock.

5. The Australian spiny anteater, known as the echidna, popularized spurs before the cowboy and caballero glorified them, except that the echidna's had the utilitarian purpose of defending it against enemies.

6. Jet propulsion is used by the squid—it sucks and expels water to move along.

7. The flying squirrel spreads its forelegs and hind legs outward so that the skin along its sides forms a parachute as it flies from tree to tree.

8. The hummingbird is nature's tiny helicopter. It can hover and even fly backward.

9. Birds can brake with their tailfeathers exactly as planes do with flaps.

10. The scorpion's tail is a perfect hypodermic needle. Like a surgeon, he uses it for injections—except that he does not much care whether the patient lives.

11. In biting, the snake applies a merciful function of which medics have known only since the 1800s—anesthesia. It paralyzes and desensitizes its prey before eating it.

12. The army signal corps would be amazed if it watched the pronghorn antelope: it signals with its tail to tell of danger.

13. Suction cups so popular today were known in nature millions of years ago. They are especially prevalent among marine creatures like the sea snails. California abalones—the

giant sea snails—have them. Their suction on the rocks to which they cling is so great that professional abalone divers have to pry them off with a tire iron.

14. Even before the blunderbuss was invented, the bombardier beetle would turn its rear on the enemy and go to town with blasts for which it has been named. It combines a gun blast with chemical attack.

15. The caribou and the snowshoe rabbit have nature's patent on snowshoes. Both have feet designed to skim over the snow.

16. The Egyptians are among some of the most ancient nations to use swaddling clothes, but the silkworm made a cocoon long before man appeared on earth.

Biology, like zoology, are considered by many to be the richest mine of analogies upon which significant inventions can be built. One of the most celebrated cases is the invention of the telephone. As Alexander Graham Bell wrote: "It struck me that the bones of the human ear were very massive, indeed, as compared with the delicate thin membrane that operated them, and the thought occurred that if a membrane so delicate could move bones so relatively massive, why should not a thicker and stouter piece of membrane move my piece of steel." And the telephone was conceived.

#38: WHAT'S FOR DINNER?

Examples:
Butter, bread, corn, cheese, squash, succotash, saffron rice, egg yolk, pumpkin, mustard, custard pie, banana ice cream, peaches, pineapple, sweet yams, quince, honey, lemonade, wine, etc.

#39: AS EASY AS PIE

As easy as . . . breathing; a dog licking a dish; peeling a hard-boiled egg; finding reasons why other people should be patient;

saying Jack Robinson; winking; going down the river in a boat; for you to take a drink; for the grass to be green; kissing; loving; shelling peas; lying, etc.

Meaning difficult:

As easy as . . . a Greek puzzle; throwing a stone uphill against the onrush of habit; grasping a shadow; sailing the sea in an eggshell; grasping the small end of a hard-boiled egg; distinguishing colors in the darkness; shaving an egg; holding an eel by the tail; for an empty sack to stand upright; for a blind man to describe color; counting the waves; jumping away from your shadow; painting a sound; reconciling cats and rats; replacing a hatched chicken in its shell, etc.

#40: TARDY EMPLOYEE

Examples:
1. Offer an office punctuality prize.
2. Institute flexible hours, making it okay to be as much as an hour late as long as eight hours were worked.
3. Offer to drive him to work on your way in.
4. Make his next raise contingent on consistent on-time arrival.
5. Dock his pay for tardiness.
6. Institute a 9:00 A.M. meeting every morning that he would be embarrassed to miss or arrive late for.
7. Make him responsible for opening the office for the other employees and give him the only key besides yours.
8. Make him responsible for keeping track of his subordinates' or secretary's arrival time.
9. Tell him it's okay to be late if he calls you and explains his delay.
10. Serve free coffee and donuts to those there at 9:00.
11. Tell only him that you're changing office hours to 30 minutes earlier. Then, arriving 30 minutes late he'll still be on time.

12. Tell him that he can work on any pet project of his own choosing one day a week, if he arrives on time.

If you produced only a few ideas, perhaps you let your evaluative attitudes intrude? Remember to suspend criticism while you are trying to think up ideas. Failure to suspend criticism is —as was aptly expressed by Dr. Alex F. Osborn—"like trying to get hot and cold water from one faucet at the same time: the ideas are not hot enough; the criticism is not cold enough; so your results are tepid."

#41: PERSONALIZED PLUMBING

Examples:

1. Add a drying room that dries you with warm air after you shower.
2. Make bathtub deep enough to stand up in, Japanese style.
3. Install TV in one wall.
4. Turning the shower on would activate favorite taped music.
5. Easily reached soapdish ledge along the walls, with sufficient slope to drain dry.
6. Multidirectional spray in shower to serve as gentle massage.
7. Fog-proof floor-to-ceiling mirrors along all the walls.
8. A special sink for washing hair without having to bend over.
9. A warm-air drying device which would start when shower is turned off.
10. Combination spray which mixes soap and water when desired, and which can be turned off to let clear water through.
11. The whole room could be a sauna.

It's a safe bet that almost anything can be improved upon if price is no object. The need for mass production sometimes inhibits the free exercise of creative imagination.

Although American plumbing has been standardized throughout our building industry to an extent unknown in many other parts of the world, it has not been without its price in terms of personal expression and comfort.

Perhaps one of the reasons that bathrooms are so frequently unimaginative and joyless is that they serve private needs long considered indelicate to discuss. It's certainly time bathrooms came out of the water closet.

#42: THE OVERLOADED DRIVER

While the truck driver was considering his unhappy dilemma, a small boy stood watching the situation. Finally, he approached the driver and said, "Your load is only a couple of inches too high. Why not let some air out of your tires?"

Most people know that a vehicle can travel for short distances at slow speeds on tires that are almost flat, but the driver's attention was fixated on the *top* of the truck—where he perceived the problem to be—not on the overall problem of getting a certain mass through a particular aperture. Also, he stopped looking for options as soon as he'd identified two.

Of course, the driver was "overloaded" in another sense, too. He was under the stress we all feel when horns are honking and tempers mounting. The boy, on the other hand, was not personally involved, so he was free to consider the problem in a calm and detached manner. That's one of the reasons people call in consultants.

#43: PRIME TIME

Example: "Mary Tyler Moore Show"

"Maid in Minneapolis," "Station Break," "Trouble with Ted," "Between Commercials."

Packagers of TV shows have obviously found that stars sell continuing series on the strength of their names. Lacking a star of sufficient magnitude, they often fall back on names based on the location of the action (e.g., "Gilligan's Island," "General Hospital"), the occupation of the hero or heroine (e.g., "Police Surgeon," "The Rookies"), or some striking characteristic of the central figure (e.g., "Kung Fu," "The Flying Nun"). The current fashion in detective series is the last name of the hero (e.g., "Kojak," "Cannon"). There are, however, other possibilities. Did you come up with titles that compare favorably with—or surpass—what the professionals have produced?

#44: THE TRUCKER'S TRIAL

Examples:

1. Wrap himself in rugs or bedding.
2. Adapt radio or TV equipment to send a distress signal.
3. Burn furniture for warmth and signal fire.
4. Make tent out of fabrics.
5. Lay out bedding to form words SOS for help.
6. Paint SOS sign on the truck.

This is a useful exercise because it obliges you to imagine alternate uses for common household objects. As you worked on this, you probably found yourself taking a "mental inventory" of your own household goods.

This exercise illustrates another important point: in time of life-threatening crisis, a fertile imagination can make all the difference.

#45: ARABS AND ROMANS

Here is the solution:

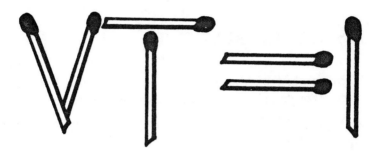

In order to solve this problem, you need to think beyond simple addition and subtraction. But, most of all, you need to be able to see the problem in less literal terms. You need to see the *shape* of the problem, and then be flexible enough to think of translating it from *Roman* numerals to *Arabic.*

#46: COMMON DENOMINATORS

Answers:
1. Boat (all others travel on the ground).
2. Skating (all others require a partner or a team).
3. Stringbean (all others grow below ground).
4. Rich (all others are attributes of personality or character).
5. Fifteen (all others are divisible by two).
6. Emerald (all others denote variations of blueness).
7. Painting (all others are dimensional).
8. Idea (all others lack conceptual clarity, concreteness or form).
9. Criticism (all others denote exclusively disapproval).

10. Game (all others involve only looking, reading, or listening).
11. Giraffe (all others are meat eaters, or make sounds).
12. Pine (all others have leaves).

#47: IT'S ALL RELATIVE

There are, of course, no real "answers" to this one, but your epigrams ought to have some of the flavor of the following:

1. When you have a daughter you may gain a son, but when you have a son, you gain a mother-in-law.

2. A man's mother is his fortune; his wife a mere gamble.

3. For some men, marriage is indeed a wedlock . . . with the key thrown away.

4. When a son goes out late at night, you wish he would make out well; with a daughter, you pray she wouldn't.

5. Tying the nuptial knot takes only a few minutes, untying it can take years.

6. A rich father-in-law is an impossible person, he doesn't know how to live or when to die.

7. A mother-in-law is so named because she always wants to lay down the law.

8. A mother always wants to be the concertmaster; she seldom plays second fiddle.

#48: CONCERNED UNCLE

Examples:
1. Supply him with literature describing the harmful effects of alcohol.

2. Promise him a substantial reward (e.g., a present, trip, etc.) if he stops drinking.

3. Take him to AA (or Alateen) meetings.

4. Induce him to get treatment at a clinic.

5. Induce him to see a psychiatrist.

6. Have him make a list of pros and cons of drinking.

7. Promise him a substantial reward at his eighteenth birthday if he quits drinking.

8. Tell him that as long as he keeps drinking he is not allowed to watch TV and has to retire at 8:00 P.M.

9. Give him $5 each week that he abstains from drinking.

10. Take him to a hospital ward to see alcoholics who have "wet brains."

11. Have a heart-to-heart talk with him.

12. Suggest to his school principal that they invite experts to speak on the harmful effects of alcohol.

13. Enlist the help of his nondrinking schoolmates.

14. Take him along to an adult drinking party and show him how stupidly those who drink behave.

15. Compute the money he would save—or could use for other things—if he didn't drink.

16. Tell him that the family car will be off limits for him if he continues to drink.

17. Convince him that it takes real courage not to conform to a fad.

18. Show him skid row.

19. Take him to see the movie *Days of Wine and Roses*.

20. Get him an interview with a famous show business person or sports hero who has had a drinking problem.

21. Stop drinking yourself to set a good example.

22. Send him to camp or a different school for a while to remove him from his friends who drink.

#49: CONSCIENCE MONEY

Any explanation that makes even a modicum of sense should have a place on your list. If you're using this as a party game or a group exercise, the prize should go to the most elaborate flight of fancy. Here, however, we've listed some reasonably straightforward prior circumstances.

1. The store offered free gifts to anyone who returned the money or shoplifted goods.

2. The store advertised that its hidden cameras had photographed over 100 people caught in the act, but those who returned goods or paid for them would not be identified.

3. The community ran a big "honesty month" campaign that caught on.

4. A famous evangelist came to town and made many converts who repented of their evil ways.

5. The store ran effective ads showing how stolen merchandise drives up prices for everyone.

6. All the stolen merchandise had tags that could only be removed by a special machine.

7. The store "went public" and many people in the community bought stock. They did not want to steal from themselves, of course.

8. The store management agreed to create 50 summer jobs for the community's teen-agers if returns of stolen merchandise reached a certain level. It worked, because unemployed youth were the principal culprits.

#50: MAKE SOMETHING OF IT—II

The drawings provided here as examples merely represent what others who have played this game supplied from their imagination.

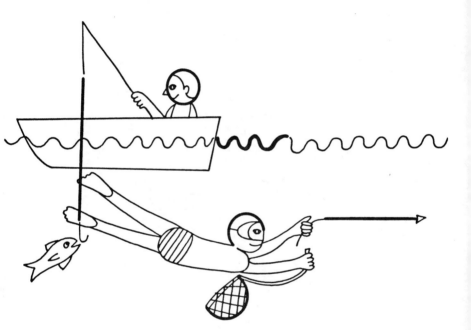

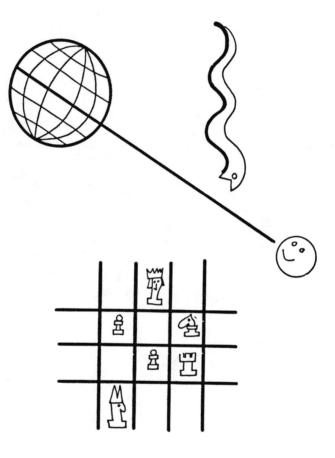

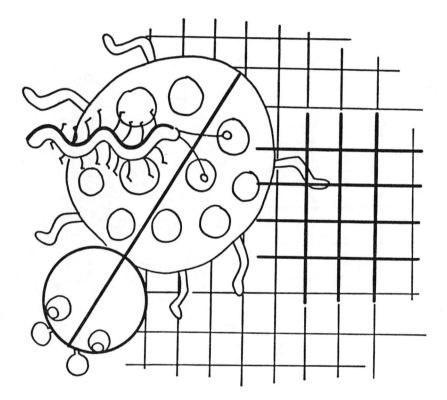

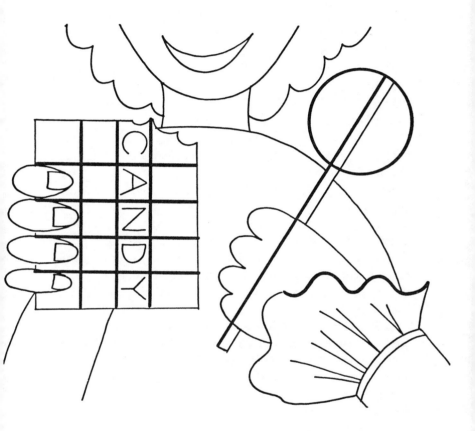

INTERMEDIATE TEST B: TIRES

Examples: 1. Use as a swing. 2. Use as a float. 3. For scrap rubber. 4. Soles for shoes, sandals. 5. Inner tube for swimming. 6. Boat dock bumper. 7. Wheel for a cart. 8. Make rubber bands. 9. Use as a sled. 10. Sell for living. 11. Make doormats. 12. In zoo for monkey to hang on. 13. End of hammer to pound out dents. 14. Use as fuel supply in furnaces. 15. Rubber turf for playgrounds. 16. To roll downhill. 17. As a toy for children. 18. Make smoke. 19. Use in obstacle course. 20. As a flower bed. 21. Patch rubber for mending. 22. As a target. 23. Advertisement for gas stations. 24. Train dogs to jump through. 25. Make slingshots. 26. Use in football practices. 27. As insulation. 28. Throw things through. 29. As a hula hoop. 30. Make a drumhead. 31. Use for lifesaving. 32. Binding to hold tree. 33. Play catch with. 34. Draw circles. 35. As a buoy. 36. Hide things in lining (narcotics). 37. As a shock absorber. 38. For lawnmower wheels. 39. Seat at a ball game, on the beach, etc. 40. Make a cradle. 41. Padding on walls in an amusement park. 42. Keep rug from slipping. 43. As a pillow. 44. A bed for animal. 45. Hold door open. 46. Plug a hole. 47. For stork's nest. 48. Ballast in a boat. 49. Lift to build muscles. 50. Use in circus acts. 51. Use pieces in art objects. 52. For makeshift table. 53. Transfer air. 54. Sit on while being pulled by speedboat. 55. Store garden hose. 56. Make ashtray for heavy smokers. 57. Bottom of table legs to prevent harming floor. 58. Make belts. 59. Dump in offshore waters to make artificial reefs. 60. Use as separators between concrete sections on highways. Etc. Etc.

#51: STRIKING SIMILARITIES

Possible endings:

1. . . . . are inexpensive and not taxable."—Sam Glick

2. . . . the less we have of it to spare, the further we make it go."—Josh Billings
3. . . . some go up and others go down."—Hipponax
4. . . . impatient both of delays and rivals."—Sir John Denham
5. . . . of very little use unless it be spread."—Bacon
6. . . . is hard to choose."—Anonymous
7. . . . it costs nothing and is a pleasant thing to do."—Josh Billings
8. . . . and like sun it cannot perish."—Napoleon
9. . . . makes everywhere its home, and lives where there seems nothing to live on."—Thomas Paine
10. . . . can't be hidden."—Anonymous

#52: WORD CHAINS

Examples:
1. Fire, fine, mine, mint.
2. Love, lore, pore, port, part.
3. Rise, rite, bite, bate, bath.
4. Came, care, cart, dart, dirt.
5. Hate, rate, rave, cave, cove, love.
6. Find, fine, line, lone, lose.
7. Nest, neat, meat, mean.
8. Swim, slim, slip, clip.
9. Give, live, like, lake, take.
10. Tour, pour, pout, port, sort.
11. Male, pale, pare, pore, wore, word.
12. Miss, mist, mast, cast, case, base.
13. Cake, bake, bale, ball, bill.
14. Mean, meat, seat, sear, soar, soap.
15. Pave, pare, part, tart, tort.
16. Wild, mild, mile, mole, more.
17. Book, boot, loot, lost, list.

#53: FIGURE COMPLETION

Solutions:

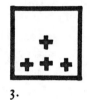

1.

3.

2.

4.

#54: WORDS . . . WORDS . . . WORDS

Chin	mere	seer	chive	rinse	empire
chip	mice	sere	choir	riven	prince
chop	mine	ship	cover	scope	recipe
come	mope	some	creep	serve	repine
cone	move	sore	crimp	seven	revise
cope	peer	spin	crone	sheen	screen
crop	pier	veer	croup	sheep	shiver
emir	rice	vice	hence	shine	shrive
hemp	rich	vine	mince	shire	simper
here	rime	vise	never	spire	sleeve
hire	ripe	cheep	niche	viper	speech
hive	rive	cheer	pinch	cheese	precise
hove	rove	chimp	chrome	price	premise
mein	seen	chirp	prime	cipher	promise
					comprise
					converse

#55: WHAT'S THE DRIFT

Answers:

1. The letters "est" move from the end of the initial word one letter to the left with each subsequent word.

2. The letters "ar" move from the beginning of the initial word to the end of the second word, and then alternately one letter to the right and one letter to the left with each subsequent word.

3. The letters "th" move from the beginning and end of the words to the center.

4. The letters "ant" move the same way as #2, but in addition they have alternately an equal number of letters either following or preceding them:

ANTAGONISM COMMANDANT CANTALOUPE DILETTANTE
7　　　　　　7　　　　　　6　　　　　6

PLANTATION SUPPLANTED SYNANTHOUS IMPLANTING
5　　　　　5　　　　　　4　　　　　4

PHANTASM ROMANTIC BANTER SHANTY ANTE CANT
3　　　　3　　　　　　2　　　2　　　1　　1

5. The letters "ro" and "or" alternate and move one letter to the right.

#56: MAY DAY

There's no hard data here, so your guess is as good as ours. But you ought to see some of your ideas—perhaps with minor variations—among the following:

1. After the long, dreary winter, the sunny days and renewal of nature contrast sharply with the gloom and depression some people feel, precipitating suicide.
2. Spring is the season for romance. Many hasty liaisons formed in April and May fail to last.
3. More routine physical examinations are done in May than in any other month. In the process, many serious or terminal illnesses are discovered.
4. May is the last full month of school, and many disturbed adolescents are devastated by academic failure.
5. June is the end of the fiscal year for many businesses. Thus, in May, many impending financial disasters become apparent. Dishonest or incompetent executives are discovered.
6. Guilt or fear over cheating on April income taxes, provokes unbearable anxiety in May.

#57: WORDS APLENTY

Example: 595 points

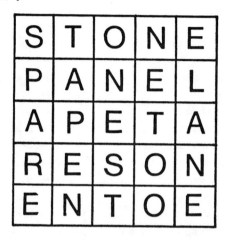

1 horizontally:	Stone 25; Tone 20; One 15; Ton 15; So 10; On 10 = 95
2 horizontally:	Panel 25; Pane 20; Pan 15; Am 10 = 70
3 horizontally:	Ape 15; Pet 15 = 30
4 horizontally:	Son 15; Re 10; So 10; On 10 = 45
5 horizontally:	Toe 15; To 10 = 25
1 vertically:	Spare 25; Pare 20; Spar 20; Par 15; Are 15; Re 10 = 120
2 vertically:	Tape 20; Tap 15; Are 15; Pen 15 = 65
3 vertically:	Nest 20; One 15; On 10 = 45
4 vertically:	Net 15; Too 15; To10 = 40
5 vertically:	Elan 20; Lane 20; La 10; An 10 = 60
	Total = 595 points

If you settled for any score less than 300, you'd probably do well to examine your attention span. Even brilliance needs to be teamed up with determination.

#58: RHYME AND REASON

Answers:

1. Happy father   — glad dad
2. False pain   — fake ache
3. Formed like a simian   — ape shape
4. Highest ranking policeman   — top cop
5. Voyage by a large boat   — ship trip
6. Corpulent feline   — fat cat
7. Melancholy fellow   — sad lad
8. Clever beginning   — smart start
9. Heavy and unbroken slumber   — deep sleep
10. Crazy custom   — mad fad
11. Lengthy melody   — long song
12. Weak man   — frail male
13. Instruction at the seashore   — beach teach
14. Criticism lacking in effectiveness   — weak critique
15. A person who murders for pleasurable excitement   — thriller killer
16. Musical string instrument with full, rich and soft sounds   — mellow cello
17. Courageous person who is owned as property by another   — brave slave
18. Mature complaint   — ripe gripe
19. Strange hair growing on the lower part of a man's face   — weird beard
20. Drooping marine crustacean   — limp shrimp
21. A man, short in height, accompanying a woman   — short escort

#59: DISTANT RELATIONS

Answers:

1. DOG   (other possibilities: dog tag, hot dog, dog ear, dog collar).

2. WOLF   (wolf dog, wolf club, wolfhound, wolf spider).
3. SEX   (sex hormone, weaker sex, sex chromosome, sex linkage).
4. STRIKE   (strikebreaker, strike up, strike plate, on strike).
5. MUSIC   (music hall, make music, music drama, face music).
6. SICK   (sickbed, sick headache, sickroom, sick pay).
7. BOOK   (bookend, make book, book club, book matches).
8. BOX   (box in, boxcar, box coat, box score).
9. WASTE   (waste away, wastepaper, waste time, waste product).
10. SPRING   (spring mattress, springboard, spring fever, spring tide).
11. FINGER   (finger mark, finger post, fingertip, finger wave).
12. BONE   (bone up, bone-dry, bonehead, bone cancer).
13. FIRE   (fire escape, fire extinguisher, fire alarm, fire away).
14. LIGHT   (light into, light out, light adaptation, light-fingered).
15. ILL   (ill will, ill-mannered, ill-suited, ill-treat).
16. CITY   (city chicken, city slicker, city-state, sin city).
17. WIRE   (wire glass, wire netting, wire recorder, wireworm).
18. GO   (go-ahead, go over, go against, no go).
19. BODY   (advisory body, heavenly body, body check, body snatcher).
20. DUTCH   (go dutch, dutch bob, dutch door, in dutch).

#60: IN AND OUT LETTERS

The key to this problem lies not in some complex interrelationship of numbers of vowels and consonants, but in the shape of the letters themselves. Letters with straight lines belong inside the circle, letters with curved lines, outside.

One of the secrets of problem-solving and one of the basic tenets of the scientific method is that you must always look for the simplest explanation that will account for all the facts of observations. Similarly, when a problem is presented visually, it pays to look for simple patterns before "intellectualizing" the data. Always move from the simple to the complex. It's much more difficult to move in the other direction.

#61: A STICKY PROBLEM

Sample Solutions:

1. Each family could buy an in-sink waste disposer for garbage and put burnable trash in the trunk of the car until it was full. Then a family member could take it to the dump.

2. The residents of each four-block area could jointly buy a truck, which each block would have use of every fourth day. Responsibility for loading and driving would rotate on a schedule. If you chose not to do it, you'd have to pay a substitute.

3. You and your neighbors could contract with a private firm that serves industrial plants, to remove garbage and trash for a fee.

4. You could withhold taxes to put pressure on the government to resume services, or start a class action suit on behalf of all the community.

5. You could bury the garbage in your garden and bale all the paper waste and give it to a paper company in exchange for picking it up.

6. You could sell your house and move to another community.

7. You could see a good business opportunity here, retire, and set up your own private trash-collecting company.

#62: HIDDEN ORCHESTRA

Answers: 1. Castanet. 2. Tuba 3. Oboe. 4. Spinet. 5. Mandolin. 6. Cello. 7. Banjo. 8. Bugle. 9. Accordion. 10. Bassoon. 11. Piano. 12. Cornet. 13. Organ. 14. Lyre. 15. Horn. 16. Lute.

#63: THE COMPULSIVE SMOKER

Answer: Six hours. After having smoked his five cigarettes, he has another five butts, which would make another cigarette.

#64: DRAW YOUR WATCH

This exercise is an illustration of overfamiliarity. It would be difficult to think of an object most of us look at more frequently each day than our watch. We look at it so often that we *cease* to look at it.

Whenever behavior becomes automatic, or we take objects too much for granted, we cease to observe them—and observation is vital to creative problem-solving.

Try this experiment on yourself or on a friend. Without looking at a telephone, indicate what letters and/or numbers appear opposite the first finger hole on a dial telephone, or on top of the first button on a pushbutton telephone.

#65: SPELL IT OUT

Solution of this puzzle requires translating the numbers into equivalent words, and arranging those words alphabetically, thus:

18	11	15	14
eighteen	eleven	fifteen	fourteen
19	17	16	13
nineteen	seventeen	sixteen	thirteen
12	20		
twelve	twenty		

To arrive at this solution, you have to ask "What do those symbols *sound* like?"

#66: WHAT WOULD HAPPEN IF—II

Examples:
1. Prime TV time would last all night.
2. Restaurants would never close.
3. Businesses could double production with the same workers.
4. Beds would become associated with sex only, and might be redesigned for this function only.

174

5. Courses teaching relaxation and meditation techniques would mushroom.
6. Firms manufacturing sleeping medication would go out of business.
7. You could work a forty-hour week in less than two days.
8. Book, record, and game sales would increase.
9. Cities would be lit brightly all night long.
10. Burglaries would be almost eliminated.
11. Therapeutic techniques employing dream-interpretation would belong to the archaic past.
12. For many, the feelings of boredom and ennui would become insufferable.

#67: OCCUPATIONS

Examples: Saboteur, saddler, safecracker, sailor, saloonkeeper, salvager, sawyer, scalper, scavenger, scholar, schoolmaster, schoolteacher, scoutmaster, screener, scribbler, scriptwriter, sculptor, seafarer, seer, seller, senator, serenader, shareholder, shipper, shipmaster, ship builder, ship chandler, shipfitter, ship owner, shoemaker, shoeshiner, shopkeeper, shoplifter, shopper, shopwalker, shore patroller, shyster, singer, sitter, soldier, solicitor, songster, sorcerer, sparring partner, speaker, speculator, speechmaker, spinner, sponsor, sprinter, squatter, staffer, stage manager, stager, star, starcher, stationer, steamfitter, steelworker, stenographer, stockbroker, stock breeder, stonecutter, storekeeper, story teller, stretcher bearer, stringer, stripper, subcontractor, submariner, surveyor, sweeper, swimmer, swindler, syndicator, etc.

#68: COMMUNITY SERVICE

Your plan of action for organizing the volunteer ambulance corps is probably sound if it includes an orderly and concrete series of steps aimed at accomplishing tasks such as:

Finding out what communities nearby have undertaken projects of the same sort, and making arrangements to visit those responsible.

Asking equipment manufacturers to "educate" you.

Approaching leaders of medical community for advice and support.

Determining who has the skills you lack. The orderly way to proceed is to make a chart of all the talents you need to get the task done, and find a name to fill each blank. Who knows how to maintain vehicles? A local garage man? The fleet manager for the cab company? Who knows how to staff and run a switchboard? Who is your community's best fund-raiser?

#69: UPENDED BOTTLE

There are two possible solutions to this problem, both of which are arrived at by lateral thinking. Neither involves moving the bottle in any unusual sense.

The first one is to roll the bill in a tight curl *against* the neck of the bottle, which results in gradually pulling the bill from underneath. The cylinder formed by the rolling bill prevents the bottle from creeping toward you.

The second solution is to set up a rhythmic pounding on the table with your fist. The vibration must be hard enough to separate the bill and the bottle for a series of fractional seconds as you slide the bill slowly toward you. Of course, if you pound too intensely or irregularly, you will upset the bottle.

#70: INSTANT IMAGINATION

Example: Unfinished letter and room in disarray.

A young wife of a wealthy businessman was tired of her marriage and had decided to run away. Since her husband was on a business trip, she decided to write him a farewell note, explaining the reasons for her action.

She was about halfway through her letter when three men broke into the room and demanded to know where the money and jewelry were. She recognized one of the men as being her husband's former business associate. She pleaded and tried to reason with them, but to no avail. After they had tied her to a chair, they proceeded to look for the valuables, and in their haste threw everything on the floor.

After they had found most of the valuables, they headed for the car. Since she had recognized one of them, they decided to take her along.

When the husband got home, he found the room in a terrible disarray. On the writing table, however, he also found his wife's note. Although she had been interrupted in the middle of a sentence, she had managed to scribble down the name of her husband's former associate.

This important clue helped him and the detectives to rescue the wife the next morning. The wife was so grateful to see her husband that she decided to give the marriage another try.

#71: MANY THINGS

The wise man said: "You said of the bed that it gives you rest. But so does the earth give you rest as your oldest bed, and rest you shall find in the grave. The bird rests in the branches of the tree, the sword rests in the sheath from the activities of war, the monk rests in the cell, and you yourself rest at the fireside. Your passions come to rest at the sight of the snow-tipped summit, and your soul rests while you glance at the calm sea. You rest at the heart of your friend, at the heart of your beloved, rest is accorded you at the green oasis, you rest on the back of the camel and on board the ship. Why do you search for many things when there is always one thing which is common to all things?"

The king said: "Because it is nowhere displayed."

The wise man replied: "Yes, but so is the bed nothing but a bed, and the rest which it accords you is nowhere displayed. And so it is with all these things. They are there, and they do not display their significance unless you yourself bring the significance to the things you behold."

#72: IDEATION

Examples:

In conformity there is no room left for creativity.

Depression and creativity make uncomfortable bedfellows.

Every creative person is a child at heart.

Abandon the trodden path, you're apt to find something new.

The man with a great new idea may very well be considered a lunatic until his idea is accepted by society and succeeds.

It astounds a practical man whose feet are firmly planted on the ground to see a man whose head is in the clouds make a bundle.

Open your eyes and look around, thousands of hidden ideas may pop into view.

Nothing blocks creativity more than the fear of failure.

#73: BECOME AN APPLE

This exercise vastly increases your ability to use *total imagery*. Chances are you were able to enjoy the real apple with heightened sensory awareness. If, however, you had trouble with that portion of the exercise where you were asked to imagine that you are the apple you just ate, and the following sections, it would be advisable to repeat the entire exercise again at some future time.

#74: OBJECTION OVERRULED

Who knows what will finally make the sale? In both cases, whichever problem you chose, you have two basic tasks. The first is to identify the benefits to you and to the others involved— self-renewal, freedom from distraction, the possibility of doing important things that otherwise won't get done, and so on. The second is to persuade the audience that your heart is pure and that your motives are just what they seem to be. If that proves to be an insurmountable task, you might consider providing a mechanism by which to keep them reassured. A series of daily phone calls or a weekly progress report might just do the trick. Good luck.

#75: SOLVE YOUR PERSONAL PROBLEMS

Remember that if your problems seem insoluble, you may have stated them too narrowly or incorrectly. For example, a problem that is stated, "My spouse annoys me," permits a far narrower range of solutions than, "How can my husband/wife and I learn to get along better together?" Similarly, "There isn't enough time to do the things I want," isn't very helpful because it puts the blame on "time," which is unlikely to cooperate in a solution. The same frustration is better expressed as "How can I reorganize my priorities to give me more time to do the things I want?"

The very act of defining your problems creatively and writing them down may help you achieve fresh and felicitous insights.

POST-TEST: PINS AND NEEDLES

Examples: 1. To remove splinter. 2. Pin paper on the wall. 3. Use as a toothpick. 4. Stick someone to wake him up. 5. To puncture blister. 6. Break balloons. 7. Open glue tube. 8. Tack things to bulletin board. 9. Pin butterflies. 10. String pearls. 11. Clean top of salt shaker. 12. Clean comb. 13. Prick skin. 14. Punch holes in paper. 15. Open locks. 16. Use for decoration. 17. Use as a weapon. 18. As a fish lure. 19. Put things on map. 20. Untie knots. 21. Sew clothes. 22. Clean fingernails. 23. Carve words in wood. 24. Clean small objects. 25. Pry things open. 26. As a picture hanger. 27. Puncture tire. 28. Hold dress or skirt together. 29. Hold papers together. 30. Sell for living. 31. Sew buttons on. 32. Kill insects. 33. Get dirt out of ring. 34. Use for engraving. 35. Mark stitches in knitting. 36. Hang up skirt. 37. Use as a clothespin. 38. Repair something. 39. Scratch furniture. 40. As a letter opener. 41. Make doorbells stick. 42. As a scrap metal. 43. Demonstrate magnet. 44. Make fine lines in drawing. 45. Hold eyeglasses together. 46. As a prop. 47. Pull string through a narrow opening. 48. Hold message on door. 49. Keep windowshade up. 50. Pierce ears for earrings. 51. Prick babies. 52. Use as a poison dart. 53. Get money out of piggy bank. 54. Play "pin tail on the donkey." 55. In lieu of phonograph needle. 56. Puncture leather. 57. Pick off fingernail polish. 58. Use as a nail. 59. Torture flies. 60. Clean pipe, cigarette holder. 61. Make cardboard filter. 62. Remove thread. 63. Dig small hole. 64. Make bed for fakir to lie on. 65. Stick in cushion to make a toy hedgehog. 66. Fasten something with. 67. Make pinwheel. 68. Use in surgery. 69. For sewing machines. Etc. Etc.

Comparing the quantity of uses listed on the post-test with the number of uses on the pre-test, most individuals register at least a 30 percent gain. Some people even show an increase of over 300 percent in their ability to generate ideas.

GUIDEPOSTS TO CREATIVE PROBLEM SOLVING

Now that you have completed the games and exercises, you will discover that you have not only developed and released your creative powers, but have—in addition—developed a *habit* of tackling and overcoming concrete problems successfully.

To plug you more firmly into a direct and uncluttered pipeline to success in both your personal and business life, and to increase the acuteness of your trained eye to spot creative opportunity in whatever you do, here are six *guideposts* to help you along.

Guidepost Number One: Stretch Your Horizons

One mainspring of creative power is a broad background of accumulated knowledge. The person with a knowledge of many fields and things can spot analogous situations and find creative ideas. The person with a detailed knowledge only of his special field or interest limits his creativity by the narrowness of his focus.

Thorough immersion in one field has to be coupled with a breadth of experience and knowledge in many other fields. To increase the fund of your total experience you can:

SET TIME ASIDE TO READ IN OTHER FIELDS. This will broaden your perspective and provide you with new information.

Start with related fields and gradually spread to areas farther removed from your specialty. Keep this question in mind while reading: "How might I be able to use this?" Take notes while reading. Anything that strikes you as significant, stimulating, or interesting should be preserved for later reference.

COLLECT AND FILE CLIPPINGS, NOTES, AND IDEAS THAT SEEM ORIGINAL. Keep them organized and available. Look them over occasionally to stimulate your idea production.

ATTEMPT TO WORK OR WRITE ON A PROBLEM OUTSIDE YOUR OWN FIELD. This will increase your ability to incorporate new information and ideas into your own problems.

MOVE ABOUT AND EXCHANGE IDEAS WITH OTHERS. Creativity is contagious and such exchanges may spark new ideas for you.

LISTEN TO COMMENTS AND COMPLAINTS. Be alert for noting the unusual.

CULTIVATE HOBBIES LIKE PUZZLE SOLVING, CHESS, AND BRIDGE. Aside from exercising your problem-solving abilities, they help you relax and frequently open your conscious mind to the flashes of insight and hunches lodged in your subconscious. Keep in mind that constructing and building hobbies are more stimulating creatively than collecting hobbies.

Travel stimulates in the same manner as hobbies. Any kind of relaxation permits unconscious ideas to emerge.

Unremitting, continual exercise of your creative powers is necessary. For this reason try to approach every problem you encounter as imaginatively and creatively as you can. Observe things around you with the questioning attitude: "How could this be done differently or better?" You should also form the habit of asking yourself questions about as many facets of the problem as you can.

Guidepost Number Two: Cultivate Your Field

Although the creative person should have a broad background, he can't afford to neglect his own field. He has to have more than the mere skill to manipulate the things he works with. He has to have an intimate knowledge of the basic principles and fundamental concepts of his field of specialization or interest. Deep understanding of your field will allow you to bring a multitude of approaches to any specific problem.

Experience shows you can increase your understanding of your area of work if you:

SEEK OUT ALL AVAILABLE SOURCES OF INFORMATION. Talk to others about your problem and listen attentively to what they have to say. Personal exposure to things, personal experience through seeing, hearing, and feeling will increase your creative powers. All successful, outstanding creative people know the importance of personal investigations.

READ AND EXAMINE THE LITERATURE IN YOUR FIELD. Keep both a critical and imaginative attitude. Be aware that what you read is not the last word on the subject, or even the best possible position. Findings and facts are fluid and dynamic and they change frequently.

George Bernard Shaw had a high opinion of his tailor because he took Shaw's measurements each time he had a suit or coat made. Everyone else Shaw dealt with expected old measurements to go right on fitting him year after year. The same applies to facts. Since facts refer to situations and since situations are always in a state of flux, facts never remain static.

QUESTION EVERY ACCEPTED ASSUMPTION ABOUT YOUR PROBLEM. How did they emerge? Who made them? How valid are they really? Strong beliefs and inaccurate assumptions are frequently treated as established facts or self-evident truths. They can stifle the creative process even before it gets started.

DON'T BE TOO QUICK TO THROW OUT UNORTH-
ODOX OR UNUSUAL IDEAS. Don't try to demonstrate
how untenable they are. Think of minor changes that would
make them practical.

LOOK FOR THE KEY FACTORS OF YOUR PROBLEM
AND TRY TO ISOLATE THEM. Remember that lack of
thorough analysis of your problem may often cost you invaluable
hours spent on a wrong problem or on a side issue not really relevant to your problem. Don't be discourged in advance because
others who had tried to solve the same problem have failed.
Remember that conditions change, and what did not work once
might work now.

If your problem requires further study and the mastery of
new knowledge, don't discard the problem. Rather, proceed to
put in as much effort as you can in learning the requisite materi-
als to achieve the solution. The rewards of effective creative solutions far exceed the effort and perseverance put into them.

Guidepost Number Three: Pinpoint the Problem

Almost everyone these days is besieged by problems. So the
question—where to find problems—should not preoccupy us
much. The person who is not able to spot problems can best develop or stimulate his sensitivity to potential improvements by
asking himself such questions as: "What am I doing, or what is
done that could be done more effectively, better, cheaper, differently?" Sometimes the negative approach—"What's wrong
with this?"—will furnish a list of irritants that can provide a
source of problems.

Because of the many problems thrust upon us in every realm
of activity, the real difficulty often is to spot the *real* or *important* problems. So it is best to arrange problems hierarchically in
terms of their importance, difficulty, and feasibility of possible
solution.

You should first make a list of problems to be solved—then
proceed to pick out for special attention the problems that com-

bine your optimum interest and understanding with the importance of the problem.

The next step is to define the problem. Correct problem definition is crucial to effective creative solutions. Indeed, it is frequently half the battle. Incorrect problem definition will prevent solutions. Fluency of ideas and flexibility of thought are likewise affected by incorrect problem definition.

It therefore follows that the first problem definitions should be considered tentative. You might have to modify or expand the meaning of your initial definition several times. Frequently, further information must be first collected in order to define the problem at all. With this in mind:

STATE YOUR PROBLEM IN A SIMPLE, BASIC, BROAD, GENERAL WAY. Don't structure the problem statement too much. Don't hide it with modifying adjectives, adverbial phrases, and side problems.

KEEP ASKING YOURSELF: WHAT ARE THE PROBLEM'S ACTUAL BOUNDARIES? What are its unusual aspects, its common aspects? Can these aspects be taken for granted? These questions will help you clearly define the boundaries of the problem.

BREAK DOWN THE PROBLEM'S VARIABLES THROUGH ANALYSIS. At the same time, keep an overall view of the problem in your mind's eye.

Guidepost Number Four: Hunt for Ideas

Here's a checklist that will help you get started on solving a specific problem:

LIST THE IDEAS AND VARIOUS APPROACHES THAT MIGHT SOLVE THE PROBLEM. Take off in wide directions—amassing as many ideas and leads as you can. Note down all the ideas—even the insignificant ones. Following one line of thought too early could prevent others from occurring.

Even if you feel that you have hit upon a sound idea, don't stop the idea process. You have written the idea down and it won't get lost.

Many fleeting thoughts that in isolation look inconsequential may contain a new vital germ of an idea. Or later, these thoughts combine with other thoughts into a new meaningful idea. Remember: no idea should be rejected at this stage as of no consequence until later proven so.

BEWARE THE DANGERS OF EARLY COMMITMENT TO AN IDEA OR STRATEGY. In the perceptual laboratory, for example, individuals who make an early, incorrect interpretation of a picture in an "ambigu-meter" (a device that gradually brings a blurred picture into focus), will tend to retain the wrong perception. They actually fail to "see" even when the picture has been fully and clearly exposed. Similarly, it is a common occurrence in politics, for example, that public figures will "stick to their guns" to support a position they have taken publicly, even when it is plain that the outcome would be disastrous.

Seemingly "undisciplined thinking" in the initial stages is necessary. It expands the range of consideration and raw material from which creative solutions will emerge.

Look for analogous situations and their solutions in other areas, at the same time remembering that none of these solutions will fit your problem precisely.

Relax your binding faith in reason and logic when thinking up ideas. Let your imagination soar. See if there is a relationship between things that nobody has seen before. Reach out for explanations that go beyond your own experience. Even if the facts don't seem to warrant it, keep on speculating and guessing.

REFUSE TO BE DOWNED BY INITIAL FAILURES. Continue working at your problem in the face of any discouragement you might come to feel. Resist the temptation to give up. Patience and perseverance are some of the most valuable assets in creative problem-solving. Most successful people are willing to try again and again, in spite of discouragement. They thus overcome many failures before achieving success.

DON'T BE DISCOURAGED IF YOU EXPERIENCE A SENSE OF STRESS WHEN LOOKING FOR A SOLUTION. Without the feeling of pressure, you won't be able to marshal aid from subconscious sources or from your past experience. Have faith in yourself and believe that the answer will come.

When the problem is tackled from every angle, sustained creative thinking will usually yield enough material for you to put into a systematic, orderly outline. Frequently, to your surprise, you may have come up with many more ideas than you thought you could produce.

Even if no satisfactory solution emerges at this stage, the unremitting, sustained concentration will leave your subconscious with a wealth of material to work on. After a few days away from the problem, when you renew your attack, you may find that you are much more productive than you were during your previous session with the problem. "Sleeping on the problem" has been proved extremely valuable by almost all creative individuals. But it is always preceded by intense preliminary spadework and analysis.

WHEN YOU TACKLE YOUR PROBLEM AGAIN, GO OVER THE APPROACHES AND IDEAS YOU HAD LISTED PREVIOUSLY. Try various combinations of them. Often one idea will start you off in a completely new direction. Follow it freely, even though it may seem that the new train of thought departs from the area of the problem with which you are immediately concerned.

IF YOU STILL DO NOT MAKE PROGRESS TOWARD A SOLUTION, REEXAMINE YOUR PROBLEM DEFINITION(S). Is it too broad, preventing anchorage points? Is it too limited, narrowing your field of thought? Should you divide your problem into several subproblems and work on them one at a time?

In any case, the previous efforts at analysis and definition have given you a better understanding of your problem. Now, after you have redefined it, you may be on the last lap of a determined surge toward solution.

Guidepost Number Five: Boost Your Lagging Enthusiasm

Creative ability tends to lag after sustained efforts at problem-solving. Here are some ways to increase your lagging creative drive:

SUSPEND JUDICIAL THINKING. Learn to turn your judgment off and on at will. During the heat of creative problem-solving, criticism and judgment must be suspended.

The acceptance of proposals as they emerge from the subconscious, while one is actually working on a problem, is a delicate affair. One has to resist the increasing pressure of criticism and judgment that the progressively articulated portions of ideas inevitably elicit.

Nothing can inhibit and stifle the creative process more (and on this there is unanimous agreement among creative individuals) than critical judgment applied to the emerging ideas at the early stage of the creative process. Critical judgment at this point will inhibit—if it does not completely shut off—the forward propulsions of further ideas.

SET IDEA-QUOTAS FOR YOURSELF. But set realistic deadlines. When you set idea-quotas, be sure your time is not too limited. A sense of freedom from time restrictions is an important factor in the solution of problems, even though a subjective sense of pressure and need are there.

ALWAYS CARRY A NOTEBOOK WITH YOU. Ideas strike at any hour and under the strangest of circumstances. If you don't make a note of them, they may disappear back into the subconscious.

Don't trust your memory. We often let a good idea slip away from us because we think we will remember it. More often than not, however, an idea that occurs during a brief moment is irretrievably lost if not recorded on the spot.

PROPER MOOD IS IMPORTANT FOR CREATIVE PROBLEM-SOLVING. But don't wait for it. Pick up the pencil and start writing down the different aspects of your problem, the different approaches you might use, and the directions you might want to explore. As appetite comes by eating, so creative mood will come when you are actively engaged in writing things down.

Sometimes the effort or ritual of preparing for work may produce the proper mood or feeling tone. You should deliberately perform such acts which create the atmosphere for your best concentration and creative thinking.

DURING THE CREATIVE PROCESS, PRACTICE EMPATHIC INVOLVEMENT. Attempt to *feel* the ramifications of your problem. You should, in a sense, imaginatively become the thing you are creating or the problem you are solving. After a period of involvement, detach yourself from the problem and view it objectively from a distance. Effective creative process requires continuous shifting between involvement and detachment.

IF YOU ARE NOT MAKING ANY HEADWAY, EVEN AFTER YOUR "SECOND WIND," DROP YOUR PROBLEM AND DO SOMETHING DIFFERENT. Break off and relax. Unremitting pressure or inability to "let go" of problems sometimes actually prevents "illumination" or insight from occurring. Effective solutions frequently have a habit of occurring when conscious attempt to solve the problem has been suspended.

ORGANIZE YOUR TIME WITH LONG PERIODS WHEN YOU CAN ENGAGE IN HOBBIES OR BE COMPLETELY ALONE AND SILENT. Make a game of the images that come to you during periods of relaxation. Felicitous insights often occur in relaxed or dispersed attention.

To gain a respite from judicial orientation and conservative thinking, creative people often seek complete relaxation. They claim that the ideas they value most occurred to them during passive and relaxed states, or even under fatigued or half-waking conditions. For example, it is well known that Newton solved many of his problems when his attention was waylaid by complete relaxation. Similarly, Edison knew the value of half-waking conditions. Whenever confronted with a seemingly insurmountable hitch that defied all his efforts, he would stretch out on his couch in his workshop—brought there for just this reason —and try to fall asleep.

SOMETIMES IT IS INADVISABLE TO DISCUSS YOUR PROBLEM-SOLVING IDEAS WITH OTHERS, PARTICULARLY BEFORE YOU HAVE HAD A CHANCE TO DEVELOP AND CRYSTALLIZE THEM TO SOME DEGREE. A discussion too early in the process might make your ideas disappear into thin air, or it might give you false leads or change your original mode of approach. It might also abate the driving power behind your motivation.

On the other hand, meeting with congenial people who work in the same problem area, may give you additional enthusiasm to continue with your work. There are no hard and fast rules here. You have to discover for yourself whether initial discussion helps or hinders you.

SOMETIMES DISCUSSING YOUR PROBLEM WITH PEOPLE UNFAMILIAR WITH YOUR PROBLEM OR LINE OF WORK CAN GIVE YOU A NEW SLANT. Such people have a fresh, naïve point of view. In the process of explaining your problem to them you are often made aware of certain obscurities or incongruities in your approach that you may have overlooked before. Also, naïve questions have a surprising way of triggering fresh new viewpoints.

A few times in your life you may be lucky enough to have the so-called "avalanche experience," when ideas come in a flood after a major solution to a difficult problem. One idea will spark the development of others and these, in turn, others. Many of these ideas are related, but even dissimilar germinal ideas occur during this period. Failing to record them promptly may cost you months or years of fruitful effort.

DETERMINE THE PHYSICAL CONDITIONS DURING WHICH YOU REGULARLY DO YOUR BEST THINKING. If you find, for example, that certain physical postures— e.g., pacing the floor, sitting quietly at your desk, tilting the chair back, lying down, or relaxing in an easy chair—are conducive to your best work, you should not hesitate to use them. In fact, you should deliberately make an effort to ascertain what sort of physical activity accompanies your most productive efforts, and then deliberately assume it when attempting to solve problems.

DURING PROBLEM-SOLVING, AVOID DISTRACTIONS AND INTRUSIONS AS MUCH AS POSSIBLE. Choose a time when you can stay with your problem for hours on end, and without interruptions.

You have to free yourself from the usual environmental distractions and routine duties. Or your absorption in the problem must be so intense that you become completely oblivious to existing distractions. You have to develop the knack of closing out the external environment at will. You must detach yourself instantaneously and whenever necessary from whatever you depended upon as a stimulus to set your ideas in motion. Real, creative problem-solving cannot be done in a distracting environment, or during the rush of regular duties.

Apply the time and energy that many people spend in worry and confusion over irrelevant things to facing your problem. You can then advance much further with it.

The ability to maintain a basic peace of mind when tackling problems is important. A very successful person has said, "I'll sweat but I won't fret—no matter what I'm doing." He understands that concentrated attention and application are essential, but that tenseness and pressure-jitters contribute nothing. He works smoothly, like a long-distance runner; not in bursts, like a sprinter. And creative problem-solving is almost always more comparable to a cross-country run than to the 100-yard dash.

DEVELOP A "RETROSPECTIVE AWARENESS" OF THE PERIODS WHEN YOU SOLVED YOUR PROBLEMS CREATIVELY. Note the methods that were successful and those that failed. Try to learn why by retracing the routes you followed and those you avoided, as far as possible. Self-knowledge in the area of creativity will aid idea-production.

SCHEDULE YOUR CREATIVE PROBLEM-SOLVING PERIODS FOR THOSE TIMES WHEN YOU HAVE YOUR MOST FAVORABLE MENTAL SET FOR PRODUCING IDEAS. We all have our personal peaks and valleys of output. Keep a record of periods during the day in which you are most productive. You can then establish a pattern and plan ahead, reserving these peak periods for concentration, problem solving, and uninhibited thinking. Less productive time can be used for investigation, study, and evaluation.

BE PREPARED AND ALERT FOR THE "MOMENT OF SURPRISE." Be alert for ideas when riding in a car or train, when at the movies or at a concert, and especially the brief periods preceding and following sleep. It is incredible how many ideas and insights most of us fail to record and utilize because they took us by surprise.

Guidepost Number Six: Prepare for Premiere

A lot of hard work goes into the polishing of an idea before it becomes a workable thing. Suppress any pride of paternity you may have and continue to examine it critically before showing it to others. No matter what your position, you will have to convince someone else of your idea's value and practicality.